YOU'RE WELL OUT OF A HOSPITAL

YOU'RE WELL
out of a Hospital

ROSE FRANKEN

W. H. ALLEN

LONDON

1966

All of the characters in this book
are fictitious, and any resemblance
to actual persons, living or dead,
is purely coincidental.

© *Rose Franken Meloney, 1966*
Printed in Great Britain by
Fletcher & Son Ltd, Norwich
for the publishers
W. H. Allen & Company
Essex Street, London W.C.2
Bound by
Richard Clay (The Chaucer Press) Ltd
Bungay, Suffolk

YOU'RE WELL OUT OF A HOSPITAL

1

I date all the way back to calf's-foot jelly, hothouse grapes, and the twenty-four-hour graduate nurse.

Any one of these admissions makes no secret of my age, but vanity constrains me to add that the first two memories are associated exclusively with my mother's operation, not my own.

Operations, no matter for what, were a serious business in the early part of the century, and her particular bout with major surgery resulted in a halting convalescence that shadowed intermittent periods of my childhood. On her poor days, I was allowed to visit only briefly in the sickroom, where my uneasiness was partially diverted by the rotating vases of fresh flowers on the bureau, and what appeared to be a perpetual bunch of hothouse grapes importantly embalmed in a coffin of papier-mâché padded with fleecy white cotton. Each grape was as large as a small plum, and must have represented a status symbol in the realm of illness, for the mammoth cluster remained unviolated until the purple globules had passed their peak of perfection, at which point I was encouraged to pluck the softer ones from the underpart of the thick green stem.

They were a disappointment—quite flat and mushy—and in my opinion, as overrated as the expensive jars of calf's-foot jelly that supposedly contained mysterious properties of strength and nourishment to hasten the patient's recovery. As I was a spindly child, Miss Sisson, my mother's trained nurse, added my well-being to her heavy round of duties, and saw to it that an amber blob of the stuff sat on my supper tray as often as a fresh supply arrived. I shuddered at the very taste of the wobbly concoction, convinced that the poor calf who had sacrificed his paw to this health-giving cause was responsible for a dusty, acrid flavor, which I did not then recognize to be sherry. However, I kept the suspicion to myself rather than offend Miss Sisson, whose presence in the household seemed to hold death and disaster at bay. Whenever she returned to the outside world for a few hours of hard-earned relaxation, I was miserable with apprehension until she came back.

Even after my mother no longer needed her, she'd drop in to visit the family now and again, and it was disconcerting to see her transformed into an ordinary mortal wearing ordinary clothes and a skinny mink scarf with a tail at one end and an ossified head full of ferocious teeth at the other. And then, when I was about ten or eleven, she pulled me through a siege of blood poisoning that developed from a cat scratch, and in my feverish dependence, she became once more an angel in a winged cap and snowy uniform.

By the time I was married and pregnant, Miss Sisson had retired to her native Canada, and I never saw her again. Hothouse grapes and calf's-foot jelly had also vanished from the better delicacy shops, but physicians and hospitals remained pretty much the same as in my mother's day. My obstetrician did not hold himself above attending any extraneous malady or emergency that happened to arise, and furthermore maintained a devoted coterie of nurses very like Miss Sisson. One of these he would dovetail in readiness for each of his favored confinement cases, and although the exact date of delivery was apt to be a matter of hindsight arithmetic, she would manage to appear upon the scene with the first labor pain, or anyway early enough in the game to escort one to the hospital, where she immediately began to work hand in glove with the doctor, so to speak.

After a minimum recuperation of two weeks on the convivial maternity floor, she proudly escorted one home again with the baby, and gave unstintingly of her services for an additional two weeks, or however long one's returning strength demanded. I blush now to recall that pampered era, for by the time my children were ready to have children, everything had changed from start to finish —including planned parenthood. I'm certainly not against planned parenthood, but I should think that all those tricky little tricks would tend to take the edge off things.

2

Considering my stuffy attitude toward a number of current issues, it's a wonder that I passed my initiation into the role of grandmother with flying colors, literally as well as figuratively, since the event took place at the end of a six-hour plane trip to a small university town near San Francisco.

In accordance with my daughter-in-law's split-second calculation, I arrived barely ahead of the baby, equipped (I fancied) to shepherd my son and his twenty-year-old bride over the first hurdles of adjusting to this major revamping of their hitherto carefree young lives.

To begin with, I was secretly horrified to find both of them—or more specifically, the three of them—blithely waiting for me at the airport, and it is to my everlasting credit that I learned to swallow then and there, and without any visible manifestation of shock, the whole modern generation in its approach to having and raising a family. Fortunately it becomes a physical impossibility, when swallowing, to open one's mouth.

I had planned to stay with them as long as necessary. Without embarking on a detailed account of my misguided mission of helpfulness, I will merely mention that it wasn't necessary for me to stay very long. My daughter-in-law was home from the hospital on the fifth day, in excellent shape and high spirits. She pooh-poohed my suggestion of a temporary nurse, and said why on earth would she need one, with her cleaning woman willing to help out a few extra hours twice a week.

I attributed this admirable but cavalier independence to a youthful lack of experience, and tactfully pointed out that the care and feeding of a newborn infant might well prove a little more taxing than either she or her husband anticipated. In all honesty, however, I am compelled to admit that the advent of my first grandchild caused scarcely a ripple in the even tenor of her parents' accustomed schedule. She was soon accompanying them to faculty parties ensconced in a contraption hitched to the back seat of the car, and appeared to thrive on a diet of milk out of cans, and strained fruits and vegetables spooned into her tiny mouth from a variety of squat little containers straight off the shelves of the supermarket.

In short, no one seemed to suffer any ill effects from this acute stage of advanced emancipation except me, for I began to be conscious of a nagging discomfort, which I put down to a psychosomatic heartburn stemming from nothing more than a determined suppression of my innermost convictions. I had plenty of them, and high on the list was my disapproval of the slapdash arrangement of weighing the baby once every six weeks in the pediatrician's office. When I was a young mother, a scale stood but a twist of the wrist away from the portable rubber bathtub in the nursery, and a daily record of every ounce, gained or lost, dictated the modification of a properly painstaking formula. How, then, could I possibly condone today's grocery-store feeding of a delicate little stomach? Stubbornly, if silently, I clung to the carefully warmed bottles and sterilized nipples of a sentimental past. No wonder I got indigestion for the first time in my life.

Unhappily, a month or so after I returned from California, my do-it-yourself diagnosis suddenly backfired into a spectacular blaze of symptoms that landed me in the very real predicament of not having a doctor to turn to, and I guess it was at that point that I finally realized how passed the past could be.

Our elderly family physician had long since died, and although his erstwhile young associate was now well into middle age with a thriving practice of his own, I still, due to some peculiar mental blockage, regarded him as a mere boy and shied away from revealing to him the intimate details of my disturbance. I'd have been constrained to consult him, however, if, by a fortuitous coincidence of ailments, a close friend hadn't come to my aid and recommended a certain Dr. Winfield Smith.

As I had already taken prudently to my bed, I telephoned him at once, confident that he would tell me to stay perfectly quiet, and he would come over to see me as quickly as possible. Need I add that I was speedily disabused of this naïve assumption by the simple fact that I was unable to reach Dr. Smith. Instead, I reached his answering service, a remarkably disembodied female who put me in touch with his secretary, who informed me, with an inaudible yawn and an invisible raising of her brows, that "Doctor" was unavailable for a house call, and was, moreover, "booked solid" with office appointments for the remainder of the week.

"But this is an emergency," I protested, and was inspired to use my friend's name as a wedge.

Several moments elapsed during which the secretary re-evaluated the situation. "In that case," she conceded, "and if it's really urgent," she added severely, "I'll see if I can't squeeze you in on Thursday morning at ten o'clock sharp."

It was a moot question whether or not I'd manage to

last until Thursday morning, but in the event that I was
still holding together, a doctor in the office was better
than no doctor at all. "Ten o'clock sharp," I confirmed
gratefully.

And "sharp" on that day and at that hour, began my
re-education in the modern field of medicine, a logical
sequence, I daresay, to my gigantic swallow at the airport.

3

Dr. Winfield Smith's name was one of half a dozen inscribed on a bronze plaque outside the street door of an intensely new apartment building in the mid-Sixties on Park Avenue. More shaky on my legs than I cared to admit, I emerged from the taxi and rang the group bell, recalling how the doctors I used to know had offices all by themselves on the commodious parlor floors of the brownstone private houses in which they lived. And I remembered, too, how the homey surroundings, enlivened by snatches of wifely conversation floating down from upstairs, went a long way toward lessening one's tension, if there was anything to be tense about.

Dr. Smith's waiting room did not aim to be homey. Architecturally aborted, it married gracelessly to modern furniture, which I happen to find deceptively uncomfortable with its dispassionate spring of foam rubber against one's rear. My heart sank when I saw that the place was crowded with patients. There never used to be so many sick people, where did they all come from? I took the one remaining seat on a frugal sofa next to a florid dowager draped in sables, and fidgeted on pins and needles until my turn came to be ushered into Dr. Smith's presence.

In my persistent naïveté, I expected a doctor who would look like a doctor, but Dr. Smith didn't. He was quite an elegant gentleman, possessor of a rich outdoor tan and no trace of a bedside manner. His expert handshake welcomed and wheeled me into a chair by his desk with one and the same motion, and directly I had touched bottom, he began jotting down my life history in such fulsome terms as to encompass not only my own childhood diseases but the angina pectoris of my grandfather on my mother's side.

This accomplished, he recorded my blood pressure, peered into my eyes, applied a stethoscope to my front, and thumped me backward and forward from my knees upward. Then, with impeccable detachment, he suggested that I retire to an adjoining lavatory, and got busy on the telephone before I was half out of the room.

When I returned, discreetly smoothing my skirt and blouse, it finally got through my thick skull that the present-day conception of a family physician, at least in its application to Dr. Smith, was a complete misnomer. It would be more accurate to describe him as a clearing center, through whom one was processed to various colleagues and laboratories specializing in separate and minuscule areas of the human body apparently set apart from the general practice of medicine. In lieu of any comment whatsoever on my condition, he handed me a list of names, addresses and appointments that launched me, for the next several days, on a strenuous whirl of distressing and wholly undignified examinations, at the tail end of which I was summoned back to his office for a second consultation.

Slightly the worse for wear, what with all the liquid cement that had been shoved into me by one means or another, I was glad that this time there wasn't a roomful of patients ahead of me. "Doctor's ready for you," the office nurse said with a very pleasant smile.

Dr. Smith started off being very pleasant too. He became downright chummy over the weather, but then he changed his spots, and informed me abruptly that the results of my tests and X rays indicated the advisability of hospitalization for further observation.

I was shocked and affronted at this totally unexpected announcement. Never having been the ailing type, I balked at the very idea of going into a hospital, especially since I was no longer bothered by the rather frightening occurrence of what had bothered me most. I explained all of this to Dr. Smith and even touched lightly—and fairly intelligently, I thought—on the emotional factors that had triggered my indisposition as far back as my visit to San Francisco. Tenting his immaculate fingers, he heard me out with the utmost courtesy and attention, and when nearly three weeks elapsed with no further word from him, except a bill, I concluded, somewhat smugly, that my dissertation on the syndrome of functional and organic disorders must have greatly impressed him.

It never entered my mind that, sick or not, there was a waiting list nearly three weeks long before a patient could so much as gain admittance to a hospital. Until, early one morning, when I was again enjoying my customary state of good health, the telephone bell rang and I was crisply apprised of the fact that a room had just become available to me at the "Manhattan Central," and I was to check in at the main desk of the Private Pavilion not later than two o'clock that afternoon.

"You're fortunate that the vacancy happens to be one of our most desirable accommodations with a full bath and a view of the river," the voice concluded. "The rate is sixty-seven dollars."

The down-clack of the receiver at the other end of the

wire signaled that I was an instant too late in finding my
tongue. Sixty-seven dollars? When I had had babies at
the Park Hill in lovely corner rooms for twenty-something
a day? I wasn't fool enough not to know that costs had
skyrocketed over the years, but nonetheless I'd have
wanted to go back to my old happy hunting ground in
case I ever needed a hospital. Apparently, however, one
was no longer allowed a choice of where to be ill, for I
recalled, belatedly, that Dr. Smith had mentioned that
he and his colleagues were "Manhattan men," and the
way he said it had implied that not only was this select
little clique a closed shop, as it were, but the "Manhattan" topped every other hospital in New York City, which
was a rather obvious statistic, judging by the several
blocks of its immense and formidable exterior. Driving
past it, as I had on innumerable occasions, I invariably
succumbed to the morbid fascination of staring up at the
inscrutable banks of windows, but I had never been in-
side the place, even as a visitor; nor did I have any in-
tention of entering it as a patient, a decision which I
thought I had made quite clear to Dr. Smith.

I telephoned him at once to remind him of our conversation, and to suggest that he cancel the room immediately. As usual, his secretary intercepted the call. She
said that "Doctor" was always out of town on Wednesdays—where and doing what, she refrained from mentioning, although she did divulge the fact that he had
been duly notified that I was "going in" and he planned
to see me on his evening rounds. Yes, she was certain
there had been no error in the reservation, she had at-
tended to it herself on "Doctor's" orders. No, he could not
be reached, and she couldn't possibly assume the responsibility of making any change in the arrangements. Goodness knew, she said, it was hard enough to get a room in

any hospital at all these days, much less the Manhattan
Central, so I'd better count myself lucky.

Muttering all the four-letter words I knew, which did
not precisely include "luck," I cancelled my appointments
for the day, put my household in order, and sized up my
nightgown and bed-jacket situation, which presented the
sole bright spot on my darkened horizon. I had taken advantage of the after-Christmas sales, and had picked up a
couple of fancy French imports that would not now have
to be wasted on an audience of one. Still, small side-
benefits notwithstanding, there is nothing more unre-
warding than to pack a suitcase to go to the hospital for
a fruitless, second-rate bellyache.

My husband hovered at my elbow, not being very
much help. He looked entirely too innocent about the
whole thing, and I should have known he'd been in ca-
hoots with Dr. Smith from the start. I assured him stiffly
that there was no need for him to escort me, I was perfectly able to take a short taxi trip without his assistance,
but he told me to stop the nonsense, and in the end he
turned out to be invaluable when it came to making sense
of all the multitudinous forms I had to fill out at the admittance desk.

I have since discovered that the only way to elude the
endless delays and the reams of red tape in a big hospital
is to arrive in an ambulance at the emergency entrance,
preferably unconscious.

4

The Private Pavilion was about as private as Grand Central Station, moiling with patients, relatives and odds and ends of luggage. We stood around until my husband finally succeeded in catching the attention of one of a number of vaguely diligent gray-haired ladies who seemed to be more or less in charge of the proceedings. She couldn't have been nicer, and told us she would be with us presently, just to be seated. All the seating space was occupied, but we took the will for the deed, and kept on shifting our weight from one foot to another. "I think they're probably volunteers," my husband offered charitably.

"Volunteers usually need the work more than the work needs them," I snapped back at him. "Suppose I had a busted appendix or a galloping pneumonia. Then what?"

"Your guess is as good as mine," he admitted.

It felt like forever before I was sufficiently processed to receive the diploma of an identification band, fastened around my wrist by means of an innocuous-looking clasp that proved to be immune to all manner of yanking and pulling. I know nothing about other institutions, but the "Manhattan" type of bracelet is fashioned of an unresilient strip of cellulose that continues to nip harshly into one's flesh until the moment of checking out, and then you're entirely on your own as to when and how to get it off. However, a lot of water, to stretch a point, can flow under the bridge before that time arrives.

The first step in the involuted succession of steps that hopefully leads to the recapture of one's health, is safe conduct to the room number that is stamped on one's name tag. "Take the elevator at the end of the corridor to the left of the gift shop," the gray-haired lady waved us on our way with a smile. "I'm sorry that we seem to be short of orderlies, or I'd have someone go with you."

"Don't give it a second thought," my husband smiled at her.

"All of a sudden you're God's little gift to the elderly," I commented bitterly.

He patted my shoulder with the hand that wasn't carrying the suitcase. "Cheer up."

"Why should I, when my own flesh and blood double-crosses me?"

"I'm not your flesh and blood," he pointed out mildly.

I was in no mood to split hairs. "What's all that crowd of people doing over there?" I demanded with more annoyance than curiosity.

His reply was reasonable. "It looks like they're waiting for the elevator," he said.

I would like to believe that hospital elevators do not all function alike, but certainly the one that we were shoehorned into at the Manhattan presented a hazard to life and limb. It was as cavernous as a freight car, but no sooner had it clanged open its iron gate than it was jammed to overflowing with as motley a stampede of passengers as I have ever encountered, subways included. My hat was knocked awry, and a fat man with his arm in a splint trod heavily on my foot without so much as an "excuse me." As I have a quick temper toward small aggravations, such as being unexpectedly startled or stepped on, I had to fight the impulse to kick him in the shins.

It seemed physically impossible to accommodate a single additional human body in that stifling crush, but a few floors further up, a nurse managed to inject a stretcher table on which lay an inert form, obviously fresh from the scalpel, with closed eyes and pallid lips, and a glass tube attached to the back of a limp hand. To my horror, a visitor carrying a bag of pungent fruit sneezed twice in the immediate vicinity of the table, but the nurse didn't bother to notice, and went on talking to a young intern several heads removed.

"Even going up and down to the delivery room in the Park Hill, I had the elevator to myself," I whispered indignantly to my husband, who had somehow contrived to keep a constraining arm around me.

"That was an awful lot of years ago," he whispered back.

"You needn't rub it in," I replied coldly.

Eventually, we emerged into the spacious quiet of the seventeenth floor, and when I say that the wheels of hospitalization start to roll as soon as one reaches one's own room, I again allude only to my experience in one of the largest and most advanced medical centers in the world. Indeed, my rosiest recollections of the Park Hill could not compete either with the luxurious appointments or the rush of attention that immediately surrounded me.

I had scarcely time to admire the breath-taking view from the windows and the array of luminous stainless steel utensils in the commodious bathroom (which, regardless of intended use, I would have dearly loved for my kitchen), than a procession of nurse's aides began parading through the door.

The first one steered in a standing scale that balanced my weight in kilograms. The second one slipped a thermometer in my mouth that didn't register in Fahrenheit, and the third one pumped the blood-pressure machine up and down so fast that I couldn't catch sight of the count.

My husband grinned. "Frustrating, isn't it, Doctor?" he murmured.

Before I could think up a sufficiently scathing retort, a new battalion of three invaded the room and performed, simultaneously, the separate tasks of filling the thermos with ice, replenishing a jar of red capsules on the shelf above the washbasin, and whisking from one of the bureau drawers a stiff white cotton garment that was all front and no back. "If that's for me, I have my own nightgowns," I anticipated her, with a pleasant-enough thank-you in my voice.

She regarded me with an outthrust lip. "No matter, you has to wear this one, least ways 'til the doctor examine you."

Finality rasped into the melody of her accent, and in the serenity that fell upon the room after they had all departed, it occurred to me that a subtle absence of cordiality had marked the execution of each of those minuscule chores. Somewhere, somehow, there seemed to lurk a giant chip on a mass shoulder.

"Do I imagine it?" I asked my husband in the shorthand of close attunement.

"I don't think they get paid very much," he replied elliptically.

"I don't think they work very hard either. Here comes another one." I broke off as the door opened again.

This time it wasn't an aide, it was the floor nurse. She extended a perfunctory welcome, and said she had come to instruct me in the use of the electrical gadget that raised or lowered the bed. She did so, and then showed me how to call the desk by pressing a small, pear-shaped bell secured to the lower sheet.

Incredible. At the mere touch of her finger on the button, a voice came out of the wall, addressed me by name, and asked what I wanted.

"Just testing," the floor nurse answered for me, and it was reminiscent of a séance, the way a faint click and a loud silence indicated that all communication had been severed.

"What they won't think of next," I marveled to my husband when we were alone again.

"That's an original remark if ever I heard one."

"It was in quotes," I defended myself. "No, but really," I went on to recall from my single frame of reference, "do you remember in the Park Hill the way a red light flashed over the door, and a nurse would run scurrying along the hall to find out what you wanted? And how she'd have to crank the bed up and down for every little thing you needed to do or not do? This is certainly the age of labor-saving devices—unquote," I hastened to add.

"It's a hell of a good hospital," he agreed.

"Except I still say that with all this efficiency, one fairly robust specimen could have managed the temperature and pulse and ice and nightgown instead of half a dozen aides traipsing in and out."

"Suppose you stop trying to run the place and get undressed and into bed where you belong."

"I'd like to know what I'm supposed to do in bed in the middle of the afternoon," I said moodily.

"Why did you never learn to read books or do needle point or something?"

"I learned other things. Turn around."

"After twenty-six years? What's the big idea?"

I made a prim bowknot of my lips. "How would it look taking off my clothes in front of you if a stranger walked in?"

As if on cue, a girl in a baggy skirt and sweater charged into the room. She might have been anybody's unfavorite niece, and maybe she was, but she was also a technician, and a monosyllabic one at that. "Cardiogram," she announced briefly, with a meaningful glance at my husband.

He accepted the hint and said he would attend to a few things at his office and come back later. "I couldn't be happier about all the attention and care you're getting," he murmured against my ear as he kissed me good-bye.

"I'm happy you're happy," I told him dourly.

"You've got a vile disposition," he got in as his parting shot.

5

The girl had already placed a piece of portable equipment beside the bed. "Lie flat and be quiet, please," she ordered crisply, exuding a sense of being both harried and hurried.

"I'm sorry if I held you up, nobody told me that you were coming."

I wanted to be friendly, but she ignored the overture. "Cardiograms are routine hospital procedure," she said, as if I should have known it.

"Oh."

She deposited a cold chunk of metal on my chest, and then immediately began a spotty conversation that was quite unintelligible to me, but to which I politely endeavored to reply until she shut me up by saying she was talking to the third floor where my heartbeats were being recorded.

"Oh," I said again.

As I am notably deficient in the comprehension of anything remotely scientific, this particular phenomenon completely confounded me. I couldn't grasp how even the old-fashioned cardiogram worked, although it was comparatively uncomplicated. Your physician, who never delegated the task, merely moved a myriad of damp wads up and down one's front, all the while keeping one eye on you and the other on a ticker-tape roll of paper as it produced a flow of mysterious peaks and dips. After he flicked it off, he studied the result intently and usually told you then and there that you were sound as a nut, and that was the end of it.

However outdated, there had been an intimacy in the procedure, and consistent with my stubborn affiliation to the past, it seemed to me that these newfangled methods were designed with the idea of keeping a patient as removed as possible from personal contact. Could any machine, I wondered, really take the place of human sensitivity? Our own family physician, for example, had always been considered by his trusting patients to be a "born diagnostician," and somewhere in the back of my mind there lingered a couple of old wives' legends about that God-given gift of his. I remembered vaguely that he had diagnosed an early stage of Parkinson's disease in a distant cousin, who laughed at a joke with his eyes while his lips smiled not at all. And another story had it that he'd detected a faint apple odor on the breath of a neighbor's child, whom he immediately examined for diabetes and found it.

"Beat that if you can," I challenged the cold chunk of metal on my chest, along with its side-kick fourteen stories below.

"Okay. You can put your nightgown back on."

I obeyed with alacrity, suddenly conscious of having been exposed to a chill wind blowing in from the open window near the bed. I didn't mind the air, I like a lot of air, so after the girl had packed up her equipment and whisked off, I started to pull the blankets up around my shoulders, but I was nonplused to discover that there weren't any blankets. There was nothing but a top sheet beneath the tightly drawn cotton spread.

Although I was diffident about using the call system so

shortly after my arrival, I was really cold and surely it was legitimate to ask for a blanket in the middle of winter. I touched the button and waited for the magic voice. Silence. I had probably been too dainty about it, and with the second ring, I dared to keep my finger firmly on the bell. Still no magic voice. After a third try, I decided that call systems could go out of order the same as garbage-disposals and dishwashers, so I slipped down from the high bed and padded to the door, hoping to hail a passing nurse. Mindful of my skimpy attire, I peered cautiously into the corridor where I was pleased to see plenty of nurses, and aides too, but they were talking and laughing together in small groups, and nobody heard the mounting bleat of my yoo-hoos. It didn't take me long to figure out that I had been caught without a blanket during the afternoon shift of duty. And a good thing it was that that was all I was caught without.

I decided that as long as I was up, I might as well close the window. It was easier said than done. I banged and pulled and pulled and banged, only to again meet with defeat: the lower pane had been firmly fixed at a point where it was high enough for ventilation, but not for jumping out of. I climbed back between the icy sheets and did some pretty fancy shivering before I finally gave the call system another chance to function. And lo and behold it did, for a few moments later, a nurse's aide of an entirely new variety walked through the door.

I greeted her effusively, ruling rancor from my voice in favor of wit, and told her that I was rapidly catching pneumonia. My determined good humor was rewarded by a blank stare, whereupon I bluntly clarified my need of a blanket.

"You should by all means ring the desk then to ask for one," she advised with a strong Irish burr.

"I have, and I thought you were the desk without the voice."

It made sense to me, of course, but her marble blue eyes showed not a glimmer of comprehension. She presented me with a sheaf of mimeographed pages, complete with pencil, and said, "I've got nothing to do with the desk at all, I've only to bring around the menus, and pick them up again."

The word "menus" had an instant warming effect upon me. I love to eat on planes and trains, and the prospect of having all my meals served in bed without the excuse of illness, smacked of an illicit holiday. I forgot about the blanket, and fell to scanning the small sheets of paper with amazement and delight. I couldn't believe that hospital fare could possibly afford a selection of gourmet dishes that would have done credit to any one of the more expensive hotels. I forgave the rate being sixty-seven dollars a day. The meals at the Park Hill, though plentiful and appetizing, had been as unexciting as home-cooking, whereas my quick perusal of tomorrow's breakfast at the Manhattan disclosed a wide and varied choice of buttermilk pancakes, country sausages and blueberry muffins in addition to the humdrum bacon and eggs and toast and cereals. Tomorrow's lunch was equally lavish, and I was torn between the lobster Newburg and the chicken Florentine, to say nothing of an assortment of delectable salads with tropical overtones plus an enticing range of desserts. I knew that I was in for a rough time making up my mind, as I am subject to similar frenzies of indecision whenever I eat out at a restaurant.

At the moment I was faced with the added conflict of trying not to appear gluttonous, which is the main reason I eschew buffets and smorgasbords, where you have to pile everything on an undersized plate and carry it back to your table in full view of other diners. Now it looked just as greedy to end up with an indecent number of lopsided circles encompassing all the dishes I couldn't resist. As I was reluctant to forego a single one of them, I cleverly resorted to the device of rubbing out all the check marks around the routine items of butter, sugar, salt, pepper and cream, assuming that they'd be included automatically. I had no way of knowing that there is nothing, but nothing, more literal than the masterminding of a hospital menu, and what you don't order, you don't get.

6

I was in the middle of attempting to tidy up the mess of smudges from the eraser when a sudden voice out of nowhere almost made me jump out of my skin.

"Did you ring for something?"

I guess I must have had a sense of being spied upon and caught red-handed in this bit of cunning, because I replied immediately, and somewhat guiltily, "No, I didn't, thank you."

Click. Dead silence. And only then did I realize what I'd done. Frantically, I pressed the call button to re-establish contact while the ectoplasm of communication still lingered in the atmosphere, but a long, long moment passed before the voice came back. "Yes? What is it?"

"I'm terribly sorry, I forgot, I did ring, I rang for a blanket," I explained breathlessly.

"We're short on blankets." The voice held a distinct note of reproof.

"But I'm freezing to death!"

"Very well, if you think you need it, I'll try to round up an extra one for you."

I felt that I was justified in stressing, before we were clicked off again, that I wasn't asking for an extra blanket, I didn't have any blankets at all.

"You haven't *any* blankets?" the voice echoed, not so much in apology as in frigid disbelief.

"Not a one."

"Have you looked on the shelf of the closet, and in the large lower drawer of the bureau?"

It hadn't occurred to me to look anywhere but on the bed, so I padded for the second time across the room. The chest of drawers was nearer at hand. I went there first, and found to my chagrin—although I had no cause to feel chagrined—a pair of faded blankets stuck together like Siamese twins. Thin and slithery from many launderings, they needed to be anchored beneath the spread, but before I had a chance to unmake the bed, an orderly kicked the door open, and ambled in with a tray balanced on the pink palm of his hand. "Supper," he announced laconically.

With only strings to bridge the gaping of my gown, I made a leap for bed, and advised him to knock before entering. He shrugged.

"Kitchen got to close, lady."

The excuse didn't hinge on the issue, but it served to remind me about the window, and I asked him if he'd please close it for me. He didn't please. He said, "Lady, my job is to put this here tray down, and that's all I got time for."

He was gone before I realized that in my quest for a blanket, I had pushed the rolling table out of my reach. He could as easily have pushed it back again, but I gathered that wasn't part of his job either. For the third time, I vaulted to the bare floor, pitying the poor patients who were too incapacitated to keep hopping up and down to help themselves.

After adjusting the movable top to slide over my knees, followed by a wrestling match with the brace of leaden pillows, I finally wriggled into a semblance of comfort, and blissfully surveyed the teasing array of shining aluminum covers spread out in front of me. I had checked into the hospital too late to order the evening meal, but the neatly marked menu folded into a metal clip, assured me that some worthy dietitian had chosen most bountifully in my behalf. And then I lifted the metal lids, one by one, and sampled each of the dishes in turn. It was unbelievable that there could be such a total lack of affinity between the written word and the finished product in the flesh, so to speak. First off, the fresh fruit cup lied in its teeth—it was a weary melange of diced pears, peaches and infinitesimal green grapes still tepid from the can. The chicken consommé, also tepid, I'd have eaten my shirt was an out-and-out bouillon cube, and although the roast beef may have started with good intentions, it had overdone itself into a leathery brown slab plastered with an addled gravy that spilled over onto a mound of lumpy mashed potatoes flanked by a few spears of partially unfrozen asparagus tips. Only the "Golden Glow" salad enlivened the drab repast. It sported a sprinkling of shredded carrots encased in lime-green gelatin, and it was entirely my own limitation from childhood on that I could never stand anything in the line of food that wobbled. However, I pinned my hopes on the dessert of pecan pie. But it, also, came close to wobbling, as it was smothered under one of those whipped-cream facsimiles ejected like shaving soap from a plastic tube. I'd seen such miracle products advertised on television, but I had never met up with any of them face to face.

The orderly shuffled in to remove the tray. "You hardly begun to eat yet," he rebuked me for impeding his schedule.

"It's alright, you can take it away, I've eaten all I want, thank you."

My husband returned from his office while I was in the

bathroom, struggling to decapitate one of the red capsules of concentrated mouthwash. Through the half-opened door I saw him riffling through the batch of menus which the aide had not yet picked up. "This is mighty fancy fare for a hospital," he commented with satisfaction, as I joined him. "And God bless your little appetite."

I didn't have the heart to disillusion him on either score. I changed the subject to a huge white box on the desk, tied with crimson ribbon, and brimful of my favorite yellow roses. "I'm not sick enough for such extravagance," I scolded him, but I gloated over the firm, lovely buds and the long, hardy stems. "They're so beautifully fresh, they'll last a week. I'm going to be real stingy and take them home with me."

"I'd put them in water in the meantime," he suggested blandly.

I eyed him suspiciously. "Don't get any ideas about my staying here for more than a day or two. You're over by the bell, ring for a vase, will you? A big tall one."

I prayed—and not in vain—that the call system would put on a good show for his especial benefit. "A *tall* vase?" The voice frowned faintly. "I'll see if there's one around."

I was willing to bet that that was as far as the "good show" would go. "I'd better put them in the basin anyway with some ice from the thermos," I said, playing it safe.

"You'll get back in bed," my husband ordered. "This room is too cold for you to be running around with nothing but strings in back. I'll shut the window."

I thought how nicely we could do without a hernia in the family. "No, don't," I stopped him. "I think it's too warm, if anything."

He looked worried. "You're not running a fever, are you?"

"A hundred and six. Look," I reverted hoarsely, "it's

ridiculous for a perfectly healthy person to be stuck in a hospital, I have a lot more important things to do."

"Relax. It won't hurt you to take a little rest. I should think you'd enjoy being waited on hand and foot for a change."

"Which hand and what foot?" I muttered under my breath.

"Say it again?"

"Nothing." (Why should I disenchant him?)

A light knock sounded on the door—the first knock since my arrival.

"Now you see, here's your vase already," my husband said smugly.

I'd have been surprised if it was, and of course it wasn't. It was a solemn, owl-eyed young man with a stethoscope hanging out of one of the pockets of his white coat. He introduced himself as Dr. Harris, after which he made a small, tight smile, and said that he had come to have a little visit with me.

"I'll step out into the hall for a cigarette," my husband offered tactfully.

One thing hadn't changed in a changing world—very young doctors. Happily, many of them matured into seasoned practitioners, like the erstwhile assistant of our old family physician, but the growing pains were apt to be hard on the patient, and I was certain that Dr. Harris' "little visit" was an understatement of his earnest intentions. "Don't wait around," I urged my husband. "Go down to the club for supper and a game of poker."

He hesitated, but Dr. Harris added his persuasion. "Your wife is right, I'm afraid we'll be quite a while, we've a good bit of ground to cover," he said, revealing a telltale addiction to the editorial pronoun, and giving me the uneasy feeling that he wasn't going to let an inch of that ground get away from him.

"I'll telephone you later," my husband compromised. Exercising a becoming restraint, he touched his lips to my forehead with all the pale formality of a handshake, and left me with a cozy evening shot to hell.

7

As soon as we were alone, Dr. Harris carefully lifted a
chair next to the side of the bed away from the draft,
squared himself into it, and withdrew a pad and a foun-
tain pen from another of his baggy pockets. He settled
the pad on his knee, cleared his throat, and began to ask
me exactly the same questions that Dr. Smith had asked
on my first consultation with him, only Dr. Harris was a
great deal more serious about it. He acknowledged the
angina pectoris of my grandfather with a troubled frown,
and the long and ultimately fatal illness of my mother
with a slow, significant nodding of his head, after which
he made copious notes in poor handwriting. He considered them gravely for several moments, and then produced a hefty safety pin from a small upper pocket. This
I hadn't bargained for. I tried to yank my leg away as he
reached for the sole of my foot, but he was too quick for
me, and held on. "I want you to tell me which hurts more,
when I prick you here or here—"

"They both hurt, and I've already been through that
routine with a neurologist Dr. Smith sent me to. Besides,"
I flung at him waspishly, "can't doctors afford anything
better than a safety pin?"

"It isn't a matter of cost," he informed me. "A safety pin
actually is as good, if not better, than anything else for
this particular test. The other foot, please."

I didn't consider him old enough or experienced enough to go around pricking people, and my sensitivities were increasingly offended when he embarked upon a completely unnecessary examination from top to bottom, all aspects of which had been thoroughly looked into by another of Dr. Smith's colleagues. At sixty-seven dollars a day, I saw no justification in offering my services as a guinea pig in order to contribute to this young man's professional experience.

Unfortunately, he had the upper hand. He not only covered every inch of ground, but he explored the crevices of my ears and nose and throat, ignoring with a determined patience my uncooperative if not downright surly responses. However, I strongly suspected that he intended to include in his report something to the effect that I was a very difficult patient indeed.

My suspicions were confirmed with Dr. Smith's arrival around nine o'clock. "Well, well, well," he greeted me robustly, "you're doing splendidly. A bit on the nervous side, I gather, but we can take care of that with a sedative before you go to sleep."

With a jaundiced eye, I regarded the fresh coat of suntan which was a dead giveaway to the mystery of his Wednesdays out-of-town. "I'd like to know how you know how I am," I demanded pettishly, and almost added, "when you've been playing golf all day."

He answered the spoken part of my question with an urbane smile. "Very simply," he said. "I've been looking at your chart."

Doctors used to look at the patient, I carried on a silent but therapeutic conversation, no wonder you don't need a bedside manner. "If I'm doing so splendidly," I continued aloud, "when do I get out of here?"

"Oh come now, first we have to find the seat of your trouble."

"If there was any seat to my trouble, I should think it would have shown up in all that chasing around you put me through a few weeks ago."

"Not necessarily." He smiled again, but I could see him attributing a rising note of shrewishness to my "nervous side," and doubling the sedation.

I was probably right, because a little while after he'd gone, a nurse brought in a fluted paper cup holding two white tablets a little fatter than aspirin. Closer investigation revealed an additional brace of extremely tiny yellow pellets which I regarded with the distrust of recognition. "I don't need *any* of this stuff," I stated flatly.

"It's the medication Dr. Smith's ordered for you," she replied, and waited, thin-lipped, until I swallowed all four of the pills.

A wretched night was bound to follow, but eventually I must have fallen asleep, for the simple reason that I suddenly woke up with my heart banging against my ribs. "Who is it!" I gasped into the dark.

"Just checking." The flashlight, which had pried my eyes open, flickered its way across the room, and the door closed behind it.

"Many thanks," I gritted under my breath.

It was too cold to get up again, and maybe if I had the good fortune to doze off once more, I wouldn't have to . . .

"Now what is it?" I mumbled heavily.

"I'm taking away your thermos," another voice behind another flashlight informed me. "You're not supposed to drink any water from now on."

It hadn't entered my mind to drink any water in the

middle of night, but all of a sudden I was perversely assailed by an intolerable thirst. . . .

"Temperature, please."

Groggily, I fought the aftermath of a sedation that hadn't had a long-enough time at a time to sedate me. "It's not even light yet," I protested over the icy glass stick between my lips.

"I can't help that, I've got to get my reports written up." Cold fingers encircled my wrist. "This room is freezing." The white uniform shuddered disapproval, and didn't wait out the minute for the thermometer to register.

"You could close the window," I suggested innocently.

She was nobody's fool. "When the day shift comes on, ask the floor nurse to send a porter to close it."

After she had headed for the warm hall, I considered the likelihood of the porter never again coming back to open the window, and I decided not to take the chance. A sub-zero room would undoubtedly add to my eccentric reputation, for it wasn't likely that any of the other patients on the floor were fresh-air fiends. Their windows probably stayed sealed for the duration.

It was no use trying to go back to sleep again. Anyway, I am of habit an early riser, and accustomed to an early breakfast, which was one good thing about a hospital—breakfast had to be early to make up for supper being served practically in the middle of the afternoon. True, an assortment of tinned fruit juices had been passed around at ten o'clock, but none of the flavors had intrigued me, especially since there wasn't so much as a cracker to make it worth while. Resolutely, I'd ruled from my mind any thinking about the sandwiches and hot chocolate that a benevolent kitchen had, for the asking, obligingly provided at the Park Hill.

Now, however, there was nothing to prevent my thinking about the pancakes and sausages that I had ambitiously included in my first morning's menu at the Manhattan. I was starved, and everything considered, I had a right to be. I jumped out of bed and hurried to the bathroom to brush my teeth so that the tray wouldn't be kept waiting when it was brought in, or vice versa.

My spirits were almost back to normal until I discovered that the water had seeped out of the basin during the night, leaving my roses to hang their lovely heads in wilting misery. I made a futile attempt to revive them by amputating the stems in order to arrange them in a shallow green bowl that had eventually materialized in lieu of a tall vase, but alas, they had given up the will to live. The long white florist's box was still on the desk, and with a maudlin rush of sentiment I gently interred the golden corpses in a shroud of waxed tissue. Their short span of beauty deserved better than to be stuffed into the wastebasket.

So engrossed was I in my sorry task that I was not aware that a technician had entered the room, bearing a flat container of small glass cylinders stoppered with cotton. I jumped when she spoke. "I've come to draw blood," she announced with a macabre brevity that fitted the occasion.

I knew by this time that it didn't matter that I had had a complete blood chemistry a few weeks before, but I said so anyway.

"Hospitals work from their own findings," she vouchsafed briefly. "Get into bed, please."

She was the no-nonsense type. I braced myself for the ordeal as she tied a strip of elastic material tightly around the upper part of my right arm, and felt tentatively of a faint network of veins in the crook of my elbow. Then she readied her syringe and plunged the needle halfway up to my ears.

"You're not getting any blood," I offered helpfully.

She frowned. "You have very difficult veins."

I acknowledged the accusation with modesty. "That's what they told me at the laboratory Dr. Smith sent me to."

She ignored my amiable corroboration. "I'll try the left one."

I surrendered, unwillingly, my unmaimed arm. Repeatedly, she tied and jabbed. The glass tube remained empty. "Devils, aren't they?" I murmured. I couldn't help being a little proud of the way those veins resisted her, but she was not to be beguiled into small talk, and resolution straightened her back and narrowed her eyes. "Ouch," I screeched, when she at last struck oil by stabbing into an exceedingly vulnerable artery in my right wrist, which obligingly yielded a supply sufficient to fill up all the containers in one fell swoop.

Her mission accomplished, she slapped a patch of adhesive tape over the lucrative puncture, shook and capped each of her ruby-red trophies, and made a triumphant exit. At the door, she paused to ask, without compassion, whether my condition required a freezing cold room.

I smiled pleasantly. "It's a conversation piece," I told her.

8

The moment she was gone, I removed the adhesive tape before it had a chance to remove my skin. It left a sticky oblong which I was trying to get off with a clean tissue dunked into my glass of water, when a knock sounded. I assumed that it was either Dr. Harris, who had punctiliously knocked the previous evening, or that the courtesy was invoked by the occupational hazards of the hour. "All clear, come in!" I called happily, in the hope that it was an orderly behind a laden tray.

"Good morning, dearie. I hope I'm not disturbing you, I won't take but a minute to empty your scrap basket."

In spite of my disappointment that she wasn't breakfast, I was deeply touched, for nobody had thus far wished me a good morning, much less addressed me as "dearie."

"Good morning, and you're not disturbing me," I said.

She had a round, pleasant face with a matching behind that ballooned out against her cotton dress when she bent over to put the stems from the roses into a large bag that she carried for the purpose. She straightened up by inches and regarded me with a smile that was an oasis of cheer in this desert of indifference. "You wouldn't believe how you can tell what a person's like from what you dump out of their scrap baskets."

"Medicine chests are the same." (If you snoop, you snoop, I amended silently.)

She nodded. "And the way a room can hit you straight off. Right away I thought how nice and fresh it was in here, but most times the heat and the smell of fruit and flowers and such is fit to knock you over when you come in. I don't see how the patients stand it. Though I must say, I wouldn't take you for a patient at all. You look in the pink of health, and that's a fact."

"I am, I only have to be here a day or two for observation. Are you going to do the cleaning too?" I hoped she was, for aside from liking her company, the sun showed up squirls of dust under the furniture, and I'd noticed some bobby pins from the previous occupant on the bureau.

"No dearie," she said. "There's others to run the vacuum and wash out the tubs and all, I'm just the Relief for the scrap baskets, Wednesday being the Regular's day off."

"It's awfully hard for me to get used to this new system. The last time I was in a hospital—of course that was years and years ago," I hastened to explain, "—one person did practically everything."

As soon as I said it, I wished I hadn't. I was sure I'd alienated her by voicing this vestigial and inhuman concept of labor, but to my surprise, she agreed with me. "Ain't it the truth? I declare it seems as if there's a law against folks doing an honest day's work for an honest day's pay—not that I'm complaining about the wages, mind you, but who's fooling who if I can't put aside the savings I used to?"

"I don't think we're supposed to save," I offered diffidently, tempering my opinion to a limited grasp of modern economics.

"Ain't it the truth?" she agreed again. "It's a funny world, all right."

"It is." We smiled at each other in delicate attunement.

"I'm real sorry I won't be seeing you again, but glad for your sake you'll be going home so soon." She looked around. "No more trash, unless you'd like for me to take along the flower box on the desk if it's empty."

"You might as well," I said, a little sadly. "It's almost empty."

"You don't hardly see nice long boxes like this any more. Seems a real pity to throw it out." She tucked it under her plump arm. "I'll say good-bye then, and the best of luck, dearie."

"Thank you. Oh, by the way," I remembered to ask, "what time is breakfast?"

"Usually around nine, maybe a little later on Sundays."

I could feel my face falling. "It used to be about half past seven or even earlier if you wanted it."

"Nowadays the help don't get in 'til almost then. It's a fine state of affairs, I always say, when kitchens come before patients. The poor things hadn't ought to wait so long for something hot in their stomachs, the way they get waked up at the crack of dawn for this, that and the other thing."

"Ain't it the truth?" I murmured inaudibly.

I was glad I had thought to find out her name before she left. "You did more for me than empty my scrap basket, Mary Conlin," I said aloud. "I wish you weren't just the Wednesday Relief." I lay back on the hard pillows enjoying a kind of mellow hang-over from our short interlude of friendliness. Maybe, it occurred to me, the Regulars would turn out to be nice, too, if I gave them a chance. Maybe I'd been a little insufferable myself, what with "this, that and the other thing." I decided to turn

over a new leaf, and emanate sweetness and light to the
next person who walked into the room.

My resolution could not have been more opportunely
timed. The door banged open, letting in the sound of
tinkling ice from the hall, along with an aide newly arrived on the morning shift. "I got to fill your thermos,"
she announced, without benefit of greeting. "Where is
it? I don't see it, what happened to it?"

Good-bye sweetness and light. "I ate it," I told her
curtly.

"Okay by me," she retorted, flouncing out again.

"Wait a minute," I called after her. "Somebody took it
in the middle of the night, and I wish you'd please get it
back for me!"

Either she didn't hear me or she didn't want to hear me.
Anyway, I was right back to where I'd started—thirsty,
grumpy and hungry—and breakfast, dammit, was still
more than half an hour in the offing. I had nothing else to
do in the meantime, so it was just as well to get my bath
over and done with.

The tub was huge, and the single terry-cloth bath
towel diminutive. I pondered the inconsistency of very
small economies practiced by very large hospitals as,
more wet than dry, I donned a pale blue accordion-pleated
nightgown, complete with matching peignoir. It had been
the choicest ensemble on the sales rack, and although I
couldn't catch my full reflection in the frugal mirror over
the basin, everything above my waist looked glamorous
enough to erase my husband's image of the opaque, high-
necked, knee-length cotton shortie in which he had last
seen me.

It didn't do any harm to hope that the bed would have
been freshly made up while I was taking my bath, but it
didn't do any good either. I smoothed the rumpled lower

sheet as best I could over the tough layer of brown rubber that girdled the center portion of the strawlike mattress, and tucked in the slippery blankets. Then I slipped off the peignoir, arranged it to advantage across the footboard, and adjusted the headboard to a sitting position in anticipation of my husband's visit and the sausages and pancakes, both due at any moment. I watched the door, trying to maintain a strict impartiality in the matter of which happened to arrive first.

Breakfast won out. An orderly, similar to, but not the same as the one who had brought my supper the night before, sauntered in with a sumptuously laden tray, dominated by a tall, eye-catching coffeepot. He was halfway across the room when he came to an abrupt halt, peered at a slip of paper in his hand, and promptly turned around and sauntered out again.

"Come back!" I hollered. "Where are you going with my breakfast?"

"This ain't," he replied succinctly.

"What do you mean, 'this ain't'?"

"I mean this here breakfus belong to the lady in seventeen twenty-three."

"Then where's the breakfast that belongs to me?" I demanded in a shrill crescendo.

He paused long enough to shrug. "I reckon if you ain't got it you don't get it, on account of this was the last tray in the pantry."

While I was still gulping air, the door swung closed behind him.

9

Too agitated to bother with the call system, I leaped out of bed, flung on the accordion-pleated peignoir, and charged down the corridor. A group of interns who were about to enter a door bearing a NO VISITORS placard, turned to stare at the clicking staccato of my high-heeled mules and the billow of pale blue chiffon floating out behind me. I kept on going.

The nurse on duty behind the desk was of an age for red spots on her neck. "I wish they'd realize we're short-handed," she muttered under her breath, as she industriously ignored the lights that kept flashing all over the board.

"That's why I didn't ring," I volunteered.

She looked up, observing my presence with a start, and my appearance with a blink. "We've got two surgical cases without specials," she announced angrily, as if I were to blame. "What is it you want?"

"I want my breakfast," I said, hoping that my lower lip wasn't trembling.

"The trays have been served."

"I know it, and I didn't get any."

She consulted a memo among a pile of memos. "Seventeen twenty-one?"

I accepted mutely the anonymity of having become a number instead of a name.

"You're not to have any breakfast."

"No breakfast?" My voice climbed to a falsetto of sheer anguish. "Why not!"

"You're scheduled for your G.I. series at nine thirty."

So. That was the reason for those beastly little yellow pills, they were the forerunner of more liquid cement. "There must be some mistake," I quavered. "It's bad enough to go through blood tests and everything all over again, but not that awful barium business."

"Doctor's orders," she cut in with finality.

Doggedly, I hung on to the coattails of her attention. Even though the sausages and pancakes were down the drain, so to speak, I couldn't bear relinquishing the lobster Newburg. "I get lunch, don't I?"

"You may have a cup of tea and piece of dry toast. You report for additional X rays at two thirty." She turned in exasperation to the call board and switched off one of the more insistent signals. "Yes, Mrs. Lewis, I know you are," she ground out as pleasantly as one can grind out pleasantries between one's teeth. "Please try to be a little patient. We're very busy, I'm sending one of the nurses to you as soon as I possibly can. I'm sure you can manage just a few minutes longer."

I was momentarily diverted from my own troubles in wondering what poor Mrs. Lewis was managing to do or not do in her dire need of help, and I had to hold myself from peering in through open doors on the way back to my room. One or two of the women lying tensely in bed looked miserable enough to have been Mrs. Lewis.

In my determination not to peep, I nearly bumped into a gray-haired man in a natty maroon smoking jacket, exercising up and down the hall on crutches. Floor gossip thrives on its fluctuating quota of celebrities, dead, dying or recuperating, and I later learned that he was an exopera star with a leg condition. He probably thought that I was an ex-something-or-other, too, for my diaphanous attire elicited an expensively capped smile and a painful cliché to the effect that I was a sight for sore eyes. I discouraged further overtures, anxious to call my husband in time to stop him from making a wasted trip to see me.

I couldn't afford to lose a moment if I wanted to reach him before he left the house, but the number kept giving back a busy signal. It was infuriating. Hilda, who had swept reasonably clean until a sizable employment fee came due, was undoubtedly gabbing with one of her numerous "girl friends." On several previous occasions I had, in sheer desperation, been forced to cajole the chief operator into interrupting one of those interminable conversations, while I defiantly held my ground in some sweltering telephone booth, pretending that there were no irate faces glaring in at me. Now I could only pray that Hilda was on the final lap of her conversational marathon; a hospital was hardly the place from which to break in with an emergency call.

I was trying the number again when an aide came in and dumped an unprepossessing bundle of garments on the bed.

"What are these for?" I asked, as I hung up the receiver for the fourth time.

She said I was to put them on and meet her in front of the elevator in ten minutes. "You not suppose to wear fancy clothes to X ray," she added with a faint snicker.

I'd have defended my right to wear what I chose, but I sprinted to answer the telephone bell instead. "Oh, I'm so glad it's you," I exclaimed at the sound of my husband's voice.

"I'm on my way," he said. "Is there anything else you want besides the vase?"

I forgot that I'd asked him, when he'd called from the club the night before, to bring the tall crystal vase from the top shelf of the pantry closet. "I don't need it now, the patient died in the basin. The damn water ran out," I elucidated. "Anyway, don't stop off, I won't be here, I have to go through that loathsome barium series again."

He was properly sympathetic. "I'm sorry."

"*You're* sorry."

"Except for being mad, how do you feel?"

"Dandy."

"What sort of night did you have?"

"Jolly."

"I take it you didn't sleep too well."

"On and off."

I could hear him grin. "How about in between?"

"In between," I aired my grievances, "everybody kept waking me up. And then, to top it all, my beautiful roses had to go and die."

"Never mind, I'll send you some more on my way to the office."

"No, don't, it's not worth it, I'll be home tomorrow or the next day."

"Is that what Dr. Smith told you?" he asked guardedly.

"He didn't have to tell me; there's nothing more to keep me here."

"How do you know?"

"Because I already had my blood test before the breakfast I didn't get, and I'm having more X rays this afternoon after the lunch I won't get. It's enough to make you sick if you're not."

"Your disposition certainly sounds worse," he mentioned affably.

I admitted it. "And I've always been so sweet and sunny and even-tempered," I brooded. "I don't understand why

I've suddenly gotten to be such a harridan. You haven't been noticing any red spots on my neck, have you?"

"Just occasional polka dots of green and orange."

"I'm serious, I don't want to turn into a mean old woman. Was that Hilda hanging on the phone before? I could have killed her."

"She's very concerned about you, she was telling all her friends and relatives you were in the hospital."

I was somewhat mollified. "I hope you cautioned her again not to tell any of *our* friends and relatives where I am."

"Why do you want to keep it such a secret?"

"Because I'd like to have something more than a little observation to brag about."

"If that's all that's bothering you, you never can tell what a bunch of doctors might turn up when they put their heads together."

It crossed my mind that his facetiousness covered more than he was revealing at the moment, but before I could catch him up on it, the floor nurse stuck her head in at the door. "You'd better hurry and change for your X rays," she called over to me. "You'll be late."

"I'd better hurry, I'll be late," I relayed to my husband.

"Well, go along and have a good time."

"Thanks."

"I'll phone you around eleven, you should be back in your room by then."

"Well, if I'm not," I bridled, "I'll damn well make it my business to know the reason why."

"Watch out for those polka dots," he cautioned.

10

I am not a conformist, but I had no choice but to untangle the motley collection of clothes on the bed and scramble into them as fast as I could.

Chafing in a variety of areas, I was soon scuffling along the hall in a rough-textured and wholly horrendous striped bathrobe, beneath which a pair of clownish pajamas, mismatched as to color and size, kept slopping down over my heels. The gentleman in the velvet smoking jacket was still exercising his bad leg, but he didn't so much as turn his head as I came abreast of him. He didn't recognize me as the vision in pale blue chiffon who had drifted airily past him but a short while before.

The group of interns were at that moment emerging from the room with the NO VISITORS sign, but they didn't recognize me, either. If ever there was a Cinderella in reverse, I was her living embodiment.

I saw two patients, also in striped bathrobes, waiting on a wooden bench opposite the elevator. One of them edged over gingerly, and I sat down. We were all too self-conscious to start a conversation, but I guess we were trying to imagine what each one of us would have looked like in street clothes. "What's holding us up?" the patient who hadn't edged inquired of no one in particular.

"We're not allowed to go by ourselves, we have to be taken," the other replied.

"Here's the aide now," I joined in importantly.

The aide came racing toward us, guiding a wheel chair with an old lady clinging nervously to the arms of it. "One-two-three-four," she counted us out. "Okay, let's get going." She rang the Down button and herded us in like kindergarten children. Nobody said anything except the elevator operator, who engaged in a sprightly exchange of quips with the aide, to which she responded with much smirking and giggling.

After a sluggish descent into the very bowels of the building, we were let out into the dingy labyrinth of the X-ray department. I was a little disconcerted to find it so lacking in the gleam and spruceness of the seventeenth floor, for it was hardly more than a wide, airless corridor, subdivided into small cubicles labeled SPINE, STOMACH, LUNGS, SKULL, and DRESSING ROOMS, MALE and FEMALE. Hospitals, in common with human beings, were not above being all back and no front where it didn't show.

The place buzzed with what seemed to be a kind of aimless activity. Technicians wandered about in grubby sneakers, while an occasional rubber-garbed radiologist emerged into the open wearing a light attached to his forehead like a man from outer space. No one was solicitous of the bedridden, waiting their turn on stretcher tables and in wheel chairs. The sticky unwinding of red tape was not geared to priority.

The clock near the elevator pointed to precisely half past nine, but already most of the wooden chairs lined up against the wall were filled with outpatients as well as inpatients, all of diverse ages and nationalities, and all in various states of dress and undress. I found an empty seat and a tattered magazine, and tried to observe a decent inattention to this conglomerate exposure of physical infirmities.

Ten o'clock. I wondered what all the great to-do about not being late was about. I was beginning to hope that they'd overlooked me entirely, when a young man in shirt sleeves beckoned me into the most ominous of the ominous little cubicles.

He wasted no time in amenities. He asked me to remove my jewelry and false teeth, extending a small paper cup to receive them. A few weeks ago, a similar request had thrown me into a dither of embarrassment, as, after divesting myself of my modest adornments, I had obediently proceeded to engage in a series of horrid contortions in order to pry loose a small bridge at the back of my mouth. Now, however, I merely waved away the waiting receptacle, since I had already surrendered, on my admittance to the hospital, both wrist watch and engagement ring, my wedding ring having for some little time been marooned behind a knuckle no longer girlish.

"I have nothing to declare," I said levelly.

The technician apparently accepted the fact that only the amputation of my finger would have facilitated the removal of the thin gold band inscribed with the far-off date of my marriage vow, but he considered the state of my knuckle to be definitely incompatible with a full complement of teeth. "No dentures?" he persisted with a hint of distrust.

"None," I repeated firmly, on the theory that what he didn't know wouldn't hurt him, and certainly he could not possibly see what I was concealing in the distant reaches of my upper gum.

By no means convinced, he put aside the empty cup with a slight shrug, and motioned me to a high slate table wedged close beneath some large, heavy sandwiches of suspended X-ray plates. I dislike being clumsy, but I defy anyone to make that climb with any degree of grace, charm or modesty.

Once elevated, with my extremities untangled, the technician arranged me, arm by arm and leg by leg, and turned me over to one of the men from outer space.

I expected the worst and I got it.

11

My husband had telephoned twice before I finally returned to my room, and the lunch trays had come and gone. No one remembered that I had been promised tea and toast, but I didn't feel like eating anyway.

Wearily I noticed that the window had been tightly sealed in my absence, and the bed made up without the blankets. It didn't matter; all I wanted to do was crawl in between the cool sheets and close my mind against whatever further indignities the afternoon held in store for me.

Fortunately, everything passes in the natural course of time and events, and it was the relief of having the last of that horrible white stuff behind me that caused my spirits to rebound along with my appetite. The four-o'clock shift was in full swing when I emerged from the elevator, and I recognized the floor nurse from yesterday. She glanced up as I paused at the desk. "I haven't had a morsel of food in twenty-four hours," I announced plaintively. "Do I get any supper?"

"You're seventeen twenty-one, aren't you?"

"What's left of me."

The witticism, if such it was, fell on deaf ears. She said, in a toneless voice, "According to your chart, you're back on regular diet."

"Does that mean I can have whatever I ordered?"

"It doesn't say here you can't."

Oh, joy. I raced back to my room, peeled off the ob-
noxious robe and pajamas, ran a hot bath, and started
fresh again with the accordion-pleated nightgown. Already an initiate in the highly specialized services of hospital personnel, I had the foresight to roll the table into
position across the bed, and it wasn't a moment too soon.
Last night's orderly, whom I greeted like an old friend,
appeared with a plentifully laden tray. "This evening I'm
really starved," I told him with a flashing smile. "I won't
hold you up again by dawdling."

He gave no glimmer of recalling our first encounter,
but his lack of interest dampened not at all my pleasur-
able pangs of hunger. I lifted the aluminum covers one
after another, and drooled gluttonously over the tasty
regiment of dishes that I had ordered the previous
afternoon. Everything looked wonderful, from the shrimp
cocktail to the chocolate layer cake. With one exception.
On close and closer investigation, I discovered that all
the staples were missing.

First, I blamed the kitchen for this unforgivable over-
sight, and then the truth slowly began to sink in. But no, it
couldn't be. Yes. It could be. Wincing, I unfolded the
accompanying menu, and had only to relate the coincidence of the absentee items with the untidy erasures
which I recognized to be none other than the product
of my own handiwork.

Morosely, I downed the baked potato, which miserably
needed the embellishment of butter and salt and pepper,
and made the best of a dry roll, and gulped the muddy
coffee without the softening benefit of cream and sugar,
wondering if it was too late to try to put a little fun back
into breakfast and lunch the next day.

A judicious inquiry dispelled any hope of it, for the
slightest change might cause a major upheaval in the

dietary domain. My gloom deepened with the knowledge that I had no one to blame but myself and some streak of deviousness in the hidden recesses of my character.

When my husband arrived he was quick to notice that I seemed to be brooding about something, but he didn't give me a chance to tell him that I might just as well write off all meals in the near future as a total loss.

"Has Dr. Smith been in to see you this evening?" he asked, with what I failed to register as a significant association of ideas.

"No one's been in to see me all day."

"You needn't sound so miffed about it, you haven't been in your room all day," he reminded me. "Don't you find it very warm in here?"

"You're acting like company," I remarked. "Leave the window closed," I broke off sharply. (I had already tried to open it.) "I like it very warm."

He looked a little nonplused, since I had assured him yesterday that I liked it very cold. However, he didn't press the issue. "Any more tests or X rays tomorrow?" he inquired casually.

"There's nothing more to test or X-ray."

He said, with a heavy attempt at flippancy, "You'd be surprised."

I didn't realize until the next morning that he must have known what was in the wind, because I not only had to submit to another blood chemistry with a stab in the tip of my finger for good measure, but the head nurse, who hadn't been around to see me before, came in with a paper for me to sign. My husband has always impressed upon me not to write my name on any document without his reading it first, so I said that I would attend to it later.

"It can't wait until later," she said. "It's a hospital rule that a patient must sign a release before the injection of any stain into the body."

I didn't like the sound of the word "stain," or "body" for that matter. As may have been gathered, I am fairly well versed in medicine, having watched television and riffled through women's magazines; therefore, I jumped to the conclusion that I was in for an angiogram, and I'd seen too many actors die, or almost die, of angiograms to welcome the idea.

"There must be a doctor in your family," the nurse said, taken aback by the questions I fired at her.

"No, I just read a lot," I told her.

"Well," she hesitated, "we're not supposed to give out any information to patients, but as long as you know so much anyway, you're having a pyelogram."

I had jockeyed myself into a position that made it embarrassing for me to admit that I hadn't the faintest idea what a pyelogram was. "In that case," I bluffed it out, "I'm perfectly willing to sign."

Not knowing how the stain was going to be put in, or where it would land, I was understandably a little nervous, but I needn't have been. I felt fine before, during, and after it was over with, and I could see why television didn't bother to squander production effects on pyelograms.

My husband was on the phone as soon as I got back to my room. "How was it?" he asked.

"So. You snake in the grass. You knew last night."

He didn't deny it.

"Well, you can't put anything else over on me," I said, "because I managed to find out that this definitely is the last of it—no more tests or X rays."

"No more tests or X rays."

It wasn't his habit to dot i's, but I had more important

things on my mind. "I hope the laundry came back, and I'll call Hilda and tell her what to market for over the weekend."

"Oh, I wouldn't bother to do that," he said offhandedly.

"Well, maybe *you* wouldn't," I retorted, "but after the hospital meals I did and didn't get, I'd like to have a little food in the house if you don't mind."

"What's your hurry? This is only Friday."

"Exactly. And I'm leaving in the morning."

"Again, what's your hurry?"

"For one thing, everything around here closes down on a Saturday, except for emergencies, and for another, there are lots of really sick people waiting for this room."

"That's true, but what if Dr. Smith isn't around to check you out?"

"He'd better be."

"He could be off playing golf, you know."

"Well, he'd better *not* be."

"Oh, by the way," he changed the subject, "I might be a little late getting over to see you this evening."

"Don't kill yourself racing," I said leniently.

I was born suspicious—no matter how the boys try to keep me from worrying about anything, they have never been able to hide even the slightest cold from me—so I can't understand why I didn't guess what was going on behind my back between my husband and Dr. Smith. Like a fool, I was nothing but pleased when they walked in together after supper, taking for granted that they had run into each other in the hall. Not a bit of it. There was no happenstance about it—they had taxied over together from Dr. Smith's office to break the news to me that I would not be leaving the hospital the next day. And still I didn't suspect what was in the wind.

"More red tape," I concluded grimly. "I suppose I have

to wait around until all the reports are down in black and white."

"No. No, I wouldn't go that far," Dr. Smith hedged. "I might say that we already have sufficient evidence in hand to arrive at a reasonably accurate diagnosis."

"Now, don't tell me I have an ulcer," I anticipated him. "I refuse to believe it. I haven't got the emotional make-up for an ulcer."

"I won't argue the validity of your premise," Dr. Smith returned smoothly, "but it so happens that there is no indication of an ulcer."

I literally exploded with indignation. "Do you mean to tell me I swallowed all that barium for nothing?"

Dr. Smith's equanimity began to give way around the edges, but he plowed valiantly ahead. "The elimination of the presence of any digestive disturbance," he said, "merely clarifies what we suspected at the start of your difficulties. Nothing alarming," he assured me hastily, "in fact surgery is not always imperative, although in your case, we have arrived at the opinion that it is certainly advisable."

"Surgery! What are you talking about?"

Dr. Smith looked at my husband, and my husband looked at Dr. Smith, and then, as if needing each other for moral support, they told me that I was to be operated on the following Monday morning at eight o'clock.

I was speechless. When I regained my voice, I was utterly affronted, and justified Dr. Smith's stark assertion that I was a very difficult patient. He said, quite flatly, that he would rather come up against a hypochondriac or a Christian Scientist.

My husband forced a smile. "I know what you mean," he said.

I knew what he meant too, and later that night, before

I went to sleep, I tried, for the sake of all concerned, to analyze the complicated mechanism that made me tick, and at the same time kept me from ticking. Pride had always been my stumbling block. There is no shame in admitting to fear, or in seeking help to overcome that fear, but fundamentally I lacked the strength to acknowledge weakness, or maybe Fate had conspired to abet my arrogance, for I had lived the greater part of my life without anything more serious happening to me than an occasional bout with a virus, and a few broken bones scattered along the way.

But now my luck had run out, and no matter how I fought it, I was no different from any one of the thousands of people all over the world who were being operated on every hour of every day. I wasn't even anointed to blaze surgical history, inasmuch as Dr. Smith's discreet but salient presentation of the facts had made it quite clear that I was merely to render a more or less routine payment for the privilege of being a woman.

He had skirted mentioning the number and the nature of the specific organs I was about to surrender in the transaction, so I'd asked him point-blank if I had to undergo a complete hysterectomy, which caught him off guard. "That's a difficult question to answer," he evaded. "We can't be sure until we . . ." I could see that he didn't want to say "cut you open," so I said it for him.

Philosophically I had little cause for complaint. I had enjoyed to the fullest the varied benefits of my sex, and I was agreeable to enjoying future dividends in grandchildren. My philosophy failed me, however, when I contemplated being incarcerated for an indefinite period of time in this enormously impersonal institution. I'd have insisted on being transferred to the Park Hill if Dr. Caleb Jones, top surgeon at the Manhattan, had not already been in the works. "Dr. Smith's lined up a first-rate anesthetist too"—my husband had delved into my forbidding silence—"and nurses around the clock."

In short, all the arrangements had been completed without my knowledge or my sanction. "You'd think the Park Hill didn't have top men too," I thought sullenly, as I stared out at the lights on the river, "and with good substantial last names that don't have to be dressed up with fancy first names."

Before I finally fell asleep, the irony of Dr. Smith's departing words hit me anew. "Dr. Jones will stop in to see you Sunday evening. Until he gives you further instructions, you may resume your normal diet, and be as active as you wish. Actually," Dr. Smith concluded, "I suggest that you relax completely and have a pleasant weekend."

I had been looking forward to a pleasant weekend. At home.

12

The one thing that Dr. Smith had neglected to mention was that a battalion of interns, headed by Dr. Harris, would unceremoniously invade the premises the next morning and surround my bed in the very middle of my breakfast.

I cherish privacy, and although I had had precious little of it considering my expensive private room, it looked as if I were about to have less and less of it. Having achieved the distinction of suddenly being graduated from observation to pre-op, I had also become a prime exhibit for the edification of aspiring young medicos.

Dr. Harris enjoyed seniority in the group, along with an established familiarity with certain areas of my person. During the course of a lengthy dissertation, he laid a diffident hand over a "definite area of tenderness in the lower left abdominal region," and expounded upon the intricate relationship of cause and effect. When he had finished with his lecture, he remembered to ask me how I was feeling, and as it was a purely rhetorical question, I told him that I was feeling annoyed, and he said, vaguely, "Very good," and everybody walked out without a good-bye or a thank-you in the lot.

The coffee had grown nasty cold, and I like it steaming hot, so I forewent a second cup, and got up to take a bath. I rang for an extra towel just to see what would happen, and nothing happened, the more so because of it being Saturday, with a skeleton staff taking over for the nurses and aides who were off until Monday. "Anyone who's stupid enough to get sick over a weekend is stupid," I announced loudly enough to make myself heard over the gushing faucets. "And you'd better quit talking to yourself," I added severely, but I got one last gripe in anyway: "So you want me to relax and have a pleasant weekend, Dr. Smith. Don't make me laugh."

Surprisingly, it did turn out to be a pleasant weekend. The ban having been lifted from Hilda's lips, she unwittingly accomplished a superb piece of gory promotion in my behalf, with my husband taking the precaution to himself notify key friends and relatives without unduly alarming them. They, in turn, notified other relatives and friends, and the telephone beside my bed began to ring with gratifying regularity.

My son called from San Francisco, announcing that he was taking the evening plane to New York and would see me in the morning. "You'll do nothing of the kind, this isn't that important an operation. I'll telephone you when it's over. But not until Monday evening," I qualified, "after the reduced rates go into effect."

I could sense, from his muted responses, that he thought I was being very sporting about the whole thing, but I wasn't. My so-called courage simply stemmed from ignorance; I didn't know what I was in for. I can't say that I was looking forward to Monday, but it was rather nice to suddenly find myself the center of my own small universe, and I actually found myself humming, as, in a burst of energy, I shampooed my hair after lunch.

Immersed in soapsuds, I carried on a mangled conversation with my husband, who was trying to read the paper. "Do you think," I called in to him at one point, "that the operation will improve my bad disposition?"

"I don't know, but now that you mention it, maybe it will."

"I'd better rinse out my blue negligee as long as I'm wet!"

"What?" he yelled back.

"Nothing, skip it!"

Crucified, he bore with the interruptions until the friend who had so glowingly recommended Dr. Smith breezed in with a new novel and a proprietary interest in my condition.

"I hope I didn't chase the poor man away," she said, as my husband beat a hasty retreat.

"Oh, no, he went out for a newspaper."

"He was reading a newspaper when I came in."

"He wants the evening edition." (I'm a poor liar.)

"Oh." She settled herself in the armchair he had vacated. "Well, you could have knocked me over with a feather when Hilda gave me the big news this morning. He's really a marvelous doctor, he doesn't leave a stone unturned."

"That might apply to a gall bladder but not to an ovary," I mentioned affably.

"Don't joke, this operation could easily save your life."

"I doubt it."

She was shocked. "It can't be that serious!"

"Don't be silly, it's not serious at all. In fact I'm not convinced that I need an operation."

"If Dr. Smith says it's necessary, you can trust him implicitly."

"Then how come you didn't have to be operated on?" I demanded.

"He happens to be watching my fibroid very closely."

"That sounds awfully chummy," I murmured.

She blushed hotly. "We have nothing more than a doctor-patient relationship. Believe me."

I believed her, if only for the reason that, judging by my own hurried visits with him, I didn't see how she could hold onto him long enough at a time for anything romantic to develop. Nevertheless, she was about to engage upon some interesting revelations when Aunt Aggie appeared.

"I hope I didn't drive your friend away," Aunt Aggie said.

I repressed a giggle. "Oh no. She had a dentist appointment at four."

"A dentist appointment!" Aunt Aggie caught me red-handed in another inexpert lie. "What kind of dentist works on Saturday? I'd like to have his name in case I ever get a toothache on a weekend."

"Me too," I said.

"Tell me," Aunt Aggie gazed at me intently, "have they done a biopsy?"

"Of course not." (How could I be so sure that they hadn't slipped one in along with all the rest of the monkey business?) "Why do you ask?"

"No reason, except that they don't usually rush a patient under the knife so fast."

"It's not so fast, I've been ailing for quite a while." I couldn't pass up the chance to boast a little, but I'd have been smarter to remember that Aunt Aggie suffered from a chronic state of hurt feelings.

"Then I'd like to know why nobody let me know," she took immediate umbrage. "I know I'm just an in-law, but I always thought you looked on me as family."

"Oh I do, and that's why I didn't want to worry you." I delivered myself of this one last lie, and hoped devoutly that she wasn't going to settle down for the rest of the afternoon. Aunt Aggie wasn't easy to take, but then everybody probably has at least one relative, close or distant, who isn't easy to take.

Aunt Aggie was decidedly on the distant side. Not only was she an in-law, she was a double in-law, widow of Uncle Charles, my father's sister's husband. It was a tenuous tie at best, and one that would normally have been vitiated with the passing of time, but she was a lonely woman, harnessed to an avid curiosity and driven by a fanatical urge to be the first on the scene in the event of death, accident or illness—in descending order of importance. Maybe she thought I stood an even chance of attaining the first plateau, because she emerged from a brief, secret train of thought, and said, with a faint sigh, "Well, let's talk about something cheerful. And try not to think about that biopsy, I'm sure it's negative, or you'd have heard."

It was too late, she'd already started me thinking about it. "Not necessarily," I said doubtfully.

"Nonsense. They'd have been bound to tell your husband if there was any suspicion of a malignancy. Where is he, by the way? I certainly expected him to be here with you."

"He was, he went out to get a package of cigarettes just before you came."

"Well, the gift shop carries cigarettes, he'll probably be back before I leave." She made herself at home in the easy chair and loosed her sealskin coat, permitting the upper part of her opulent figure to pop out like a jack-in-the-box. "No sense wasting money on flowers," she said (I neglected to mention that Aunt Aggie, though immensely wealthy, was extremely frugal), "so instead, I had my cook make you a jar of barley broth with a base of good strong meat stock and vegetables." She gestured toward two brown-paper packages she had placed on the desk. "The other bag's berries; on the way over I saw some beautiful strawberries in that nice Madison Avenue fruit market, so I stopped to buy you a pint."

"Oh, thank you!"

"I don't care how much you pay in a hospital, they can't afford to give you fresh strawberries out of season."

"I should say not," I said.

"And I wager that homemade soup will just touch the spot."

"I should say it will." (Watch out against another "should say," you're sounding insincere.)

"One of the nurses can warm it up for your supper, and while she's at it, tell her to wash half the berries for tonight, and keep the other half in the refrigerator for your lunch tomorrow."

"That's a good idea," I agreed, wondering which of the nurses would be able, ready, and willing to perform these favors.

Aunt Aggie read my mind. "Maybe I'd better take everything out to the desk now, and see that it's done and done properly."

I put out a detaining hand. "Please don't bother. All I have to do is ring when I'm ready."

"You could ring until you were blue in the face at the Park Hill," Aunt Aggie recalled dourly.

Surely I hadn't heard her correctly. "You can't mean that the service is slower at the Park Hill than *here?*" I exclaimed, caught squarely in the net of my inept fabrications.

"Slower?" Aunt Aggie gave a sniff of derision. "Why, you could die waiting for a nurse to answer your bell. If Dr. Diefenbacher—he took care of poor Charlie, too—

wasn't a Park Hill man from way back, I'd have come to
the Manhattan like a shot."

I stared at her. "But I always thought the Park Hill was
wonderful, and if Dr. Smith wasn't a Manhattan man, I'd
be there this minute!"

"Maybe in the old days it was wonderful, but if you
went back there now, you wouldn't recognize the place.
Or the staff."

I was loath to relinquish a dream. "But do you know
anybody who's been there recently?" I persisted.

"Do I know anybody? I was there myself last summer.
For two long weeks. Flat on my back."

My incredulity wavered in the direction of duty. "I
didn't know you'd been ill, what was wrong?"

"I went in for herpes zoster."

I happen to have a stolidly retentive memory for in-
consequential things like telephone numbers and odd bits
of information. "Herpes zoster," I repeated thoughtfully.
"Isn't that another name for shingles?"

I didn't realize the tactlessness of my question until
I noticed a faint flush creep up toward Aunt Aggie's
cheekbones. "Names are of no importance," she replied
with a distinct chill in her voice. "All I can say is that I
have never in all my life experienced such agony. At first
Dr. Diefenbacher thought I was suffering from a tumor
pressing on the sciatic nerve and that's when he called an
ambulance and rushed me to the hospital."

"How dreadful," I commiserated, adding silently, for
my own entertainment, "'But I still say it sounds like to-
mato juice,' so why two weeks, for heaven's sake, on the
'flat of your back'?"

There followed a frightening instant during which I
was certain I had spoken aloud, for Aunt Aggie fixed me
with a steely eye. "Herpes zoster," she sternly impressed

upon me, "is nothing to make light of. I wouldn't wish it on my worst enemy."

"We were probably abroad at the time," I said, quick to mend the familial fences that Aunt Aggie so doggedly erected and maintained. "You must have thought me very inattentive."

"Frankly, I did. How's your new grandchild coming along?"

"Just beautifully. My daughter-in-law gave me a full report over the phone this morning." I switched the discussion with alacrity, unaware that I was encouraging Aunt Aggie to exhume still another grievance.

She said, with flattened lips, "I sent them a card when the baby was born, but I never got an answer."

"You know how young people are," I apologized for them, although I'd have blamed them more had they failed to acknowledge a small gift. Or even a letter. But a card?

"And the other two boys? Are they doing well?"

"Very well. They'll be here this evening with their wives."

"I must say you've certainly got a nice big room to have company in. And what a view!" She flattened her lips again. "I faced a noisy side street jammed with traffic."

"But don't forget, this location has its disadvantages too, it's not as central as the Park Hill," I attempted to appease her.

"Yes, and no. It all depends on where you live."

"That's true. It does."

Conversation limped to a halt until she aimed another question at me. "Have you got your first week's bill yet?"

"I haven't been here a week."

"Well, just wait until you see how the extras add up.

You have to be a millionaire to be sick in a hospital these days."

"I imagine so."

"I didn't have surgery, but from what I hear the charges for the operating room and the anesthetist and the recovery room and all, amount to a small fortune. And of course it's worth your life to collect medical insurance, they squirm out of paying it every which way."

"It's bad enough on a car," I rejoined, not too brilliantly.

Aunt Aggie said, "Nothing could induce me to keep a car in New York. It's different with you, you have a husband who drives."

My face was beginning to stiffen under the tired plaster of my smile. I experimented with the subliminal. "He'll be so sorry not to have seen you," I said.

It worked. Aunt Aggie secured her woolen scarf around her neck and humped into her unwieldy coat. "I'd like to see him, too, but I don't think I can wait for him to come back," she said. "Give him my regards."

"I will," I said.

"And tell him to be sure to call me as soon as it's over, I'm anxious to hear what's what."

In a moment of rashness I almost promised to call her myself.

13

"You missed Aunt Aggie by about two minutes," I congratulated my husband when he appeared at the door. "How come you were so bloody lucky?"

"It wasn't bloody luck, it was fast thinking," he said, much pleased with himself. "I saw her leaving your room, and ducked into the pantry until she got into the elevator."

"You should be ashamed," I reproved him, "especially since she was sweet enough to bring you a jar of homemade soup for your supper tonight, and some fresh strawberries for your breakfast."

I watched for the look of horror to cross his face, for he is a man ridden by small but strange resistances. I have, on occasion, witnessed his panic when a waiter starts to tie one of those gay lobster towels around his neck in a seafood restaurant, and only a trifle less spectacularly does he blanch at the mere thought of having to carry any sort of package, unless, of course, it should happen to contain a shotgun or some fishing equipment. Under such circumstances, regardless of how cumbersome or heavy the burden, he will joyfully lug it for blocks on end.

"This is sheer false pride," I told him coldly, as I saw him recoil from the brace of lumpy bundles on the desk.

"If you refuse to take them home, what do you expect me to do with them?"

I left myself wide open for that one. As an alternative, he suggested getting rid of the stuff on one of the nurses, but I said I didn't know any of them intimately enough for soup.

The orderly provided a solution when he came in with the supper tray, or rather, half a solution, because he accepted the berries but backed away from the barley broth, leaving me no choice but to dump it down the toilet. And if you've never dumped a good rich soup full of vegetables down a toilet, you have no idea how messy it can be, and how it takes its own sweet time swirling around until it makes its final curtsy and disappears.

"I hope it doesn't get playful and come back up again," I said.

My husband said he hoped so too, and we had a long, happy evening together, which ended all too soon. I walked with him to the elevator. It was later than we'd realized. The fruit juices had long since been passed out, and the corridor was full of stillness, except for the muted sound of a radio from behind a closed door.

"You'll be glad to know that I've got the Park Hill out of my system," I said, after we kissed good night. "I hear it isn't what it used to be."

He said, "Nothing's what it used to be."

"I guess not," I admitted regretfully. "I guess that's one of the penalties of growing older."

"It's not always a penalty."

"I'm in a mood to think it is," I said.

The nurse on duty behind the desk looked up and smiled at me as I went back to my room. "Would you like an alcohol sponge before you go to sleep?" she asked.

I was too astonished to do more than stammer a grateful acceptance, having concluded that the unopened bottle of rubbing lotion on the bathroom shelf was for show and not for use. "Weekends aren't apt to be busy," she explained. "Patients usually go home if they can, but I see on your chart that you're having surgery on Monday."

"Yes, I am." She was really human; I warmed to the note of sympathy in her voice. It was too bad—I could probably have given her the strawberries, and the soup, too.

I was due for a few other agreeable surprises the next day. The first one was that nobody disturbed me all night, and in the morning, a pale ray of sun was fingering its way beneath the dark shade when I opened my eyes. In the dim light, I couldn't see the nurse's face, but her voice was friendly. "I left your temperature and pulse until the last, so you could sleep a little longer," she said.

While she was waiting for the thermometer to register, she confided that she was just crazy about Dr. Jones—she didn't know anyone on his service who wasn't crazy about him, he was an "absolute doll."

So. That was it. I owed the alcohol rub and the extra hour's sleep to the distinction of being Dr. Caleb Jones's patient. I had mixed feelings, however, about being operated on by an "absolute doll." I'd have preferred someone on the order of Aunt Aggie's Dr. Diefenbacher, even though he sounded like he smelled of cigars.

The second surprise of the day was the arrival of several gifts of flowers from the most unexpected sources. For example, someone to whom I'd been owing a dinner party for months, sent an elaborate arrangement of spider chrysanthemums, purple larkspurs and yellow irises, with every last stem of them wired and imbedded in a damp, spongy substance that required some, but very little, ad-

ditional moistening. Since it was Sunday, at least two of
these preassembled concoctions must have been left outside at the desk the previous evening, but the modern
art of packaging, like frozen dinners that needed only to
be defrosted and heated, had preserved the shape of their
intricate perfection.

"As Aunt Aggie would say," I remarked to my husband, "these posies must have cost a pretty penny."

"But you don't like them," he said quizzically.

"I like opening a box, or even a green paper cornuco-
pia. Just think, though," I added complacently, "I haven't
even been operated on yet, and already the room is beginning to fill up like a florist's shop. I can't wait for next
week to see who'll send what."

I had no premonition that I wasn't going to care about
anything at all next week.

The last surprise of the day was Dr. Jones. He came in
to see me after supper, and he didn't look like a "living
doll," nor did he look like Dr. Smith, as I had pictured
him. Of medium height, and somewhat stocky, he bore a
striking resemblance to my old obstetrician, especially
when he held my hand in his firm grasp for an extra moment or two and told me that I must get a good night's
rest and clear my mind of worry.

"Have I anything to worry about?" I asked him.

I liked him for not pretending to misinterpret my question. He said, "I don't think so, there's no indication of
malignancy."

"But you can't be sure."

His eyes, deeply brown and very kind, smiled down
at me. "You're making it very easy for me."

"I've been making it very hard for Dr. Smith," I confessed.

This time his lips smiled. "I'm sure he forgives you under the circumstances. I've gone over your history and I see that this is your first operation."

"Yes, and I do have one real worry about it," I blurted out.

"Tell me what it is."

"It may sound silly, but I dread having ether—I had whiffs of it with two babies, and a real dose of it with the third, and I hated the hideous feeling of going under, and coming out of it, and the nausea afterwards."

He laughed. "I'm afraid you're a little behind the times —ether went out with trolley cars. We use sodium pentothol today."

"Is that nicer than ether?"

"Much nicer," he assured me. "You'll fall quietly to sleep in your bed, and the next thing you know, you'll be waking up with the operation all over with."

"It sounds lovely," I said quite gaily.

"Not unequivocably so," he tempered my enthusiasm. "You're likely to be conscious of considerable discomfort, but your nurses will have instructions to keep any severe pain at a minimum."

"Which reminds me, I almost forgot to ask, do I have to have nurses around the clock?"

He weighed his answer. "Do you have to? No. But since we've been fortunate enough to get specials for you, I'd advise you not to depend on floor care. At least not for the first several days."

"Anything you say," I agreed. "I only asked because I hear there's such a shortage, I didn't want to pamper myself if it wasn't necessary."

I was really quite happy at the prospect of having private nurses, for I had wonderful memories of these selfless angels of mercy, and it was going to be a godsend not to have to plead with the desk in moments of emergency, like that poor Mrs. Lewis down the hall. Indeed, Dr. Jones had so completely set my mind at ease, that I didn't feel the need of a sleeping pill.

I couldn't swallow one fast enough, though, after the ministrations of an aide, who proved to be a real menace with a razor.

14

In the morning, the world around me suddenly stopped being, and I don't recall anything very clearly except the rude wham of a hypodermic needle, and my husband saying, "Ouch. That hurt me more than it hurt you."

It was generous conceit, so I didn't argue its validity. "What are you doing here at this unearthly hour?" I demanded instead.

"Oh, I thought I'd drop in for a few minutes to see you off." He wasn't as nonchalant as he tried to sound. In the sharp slice of light from the wall lamp above the bed, I noticed that peaked look of a recent haircut, only I knew it wasn't all haircut, I knew how I'd have felt if it were he, or one of the boys, who was about to be wheeled up to the operating room.

"I wish I could change places with you," he answered my unspoken thought.

"You'd make headlines in all the medical journals," I quipped through a sudden haze of drowsiness.

Time skipped some beats, and I was mildly amazed to find that I was lying on a stretcher-table in a strange corridor, looking through an open door where doctors and nurses in long gowns and swathed heads were moving around in a white-tiled area. "Is the operation over already?" I asked in pleased astonishment.

"You haven't gone in yet, we're a little behind schedule," someone answered. "Just relax."

It was a little difficult to relax with that open door in front of me, so I closed my eyes and thought how cleverly television copied life, or was it the other way around. . . .

When I opened my eyes, I was still on the stretcher-table, but I was in a different place, with other stretcher-tables all around me. My lips had turned into thick, dry pieces of wood, but I managed to move them. "Where am I?"

"In the recovery room. It's all over."

If my wooden lips had let me laugh, I'd have laughed, because they'd operated on the wrong person. Somebody with a monumental pain was lying beside me, but I didn't feel any pain at all, except for the niggling scratch of a pin against the back of my hand. "Take that pin away!" I said with asperity.

"Be still. It's glucose, stop jerking your arm."

I couldn't see who was talking, but I resented being ordered around like that. "Who are you, anyway?" I demanded.

"I'm Miss Sosensky. Your Special."

"If you're my Special, you should have told that woman with the bag of fruit not to sneeze in the elevator," I reprimanded her in a loud singsong that I borrowed from the person with the big pain who was still lying beside me.

"What did she say?"

How odd. I thought I recognized my husband's voice coming from far away, but the first voice drowned it out. "I don't know, I couldn't understand her, she just keeps mumbling, she won't make sense for a while yet."

"I do make sense!" I protested indignantly. "Where am I?"

"In your bed."

I was even more indignant at the idea of sharing my bed with a stranger. "You tell her to go away or I'll get up and leave!"

"All right, I'll tell her, you just lie back. . . ."

"Has she gone yet?"

"Yes, I sent her away."

"What time is it?"

"Half past two."

". . . What time is it?"

"Half past six."

It was too difficult to try to figure it out. Besides, the other person was gone, and had left me with that awful pain in my own middle. "I hurt," I whimpered.

"I'm going to give you another hypo after you take a little water."

"I don't want any water."

"It's good for you. I'm holding the drinking-tube right against your lips. Just sip."

"Big deal." I was back to the intoxicating lilt of that singsong voice. "Are you still Miss Sosensky?" Miss Sosensky. Clarity, like flickering lights, filtered confusingly through the fuzz that clogged my brain.

"Miss Sosensky will be back in the morning. I came on duty at four. I'm Miss Kelly."

"I'd rather have Miss Sisson, please."

"Who?"

"Miss Sisson. She was my mother's nurse." Slowly and carefully I marshaled my words before they could slip back into darkness. "She didn't keep going away, she was a twenty-four-hour trained nurse."

Miss Kelly laughed. "Those poor slobs went out with the horse and buggy."

"The trolley car," I corrected her gravely.

"All right, the trolley car. Come on now, take another sip."

"Calf's-foot jelly has more nourishment than water."

"Would you settle for some nice pig's knuckles?"

"You're making fun of me and I resent it," I said coldly. "I wish to telephone my son in San Francisco."

"You'd scare the living daylights out of him with all that dope in you."

"But I promised—"

"Sorry. Your phone's been disconnected. Doctor's orders."

"Then I'll tell my husband to do it. Where is he?"

"He's talking to Dr. Jones in the hall."

My feelings were injured. "I'm the one who's sick, why doesn't Dr. Jones come in and talk to me instead?"

"He's been in, but you were dead to the world. Don't push me away, I'm just turning you over for your hypo."

I gave a startled yelp.

"It'd hurt more if I pussyfooted around," Miss Kelly said. "You'll feel better in a little while."

". . . I don't feel better. What time is it?"

Nobody answered me. The room was dark, except for the subdued glow of a lamp at the far end of it. A faint snore came from the direction of the armchair next to the lamp. I thought it was my husband—although he won't admit to snoring—and I wanted to let him sleep. Maybe the nurse at the desk would give me something for the pain, which was more excruciating than ever. I fumbled for the bell that was pinned to the sheet, but I must have bypassed it, for I knocked over a glass on the bedside table and it fell to the floor with a crash. The snoring stopped. A scuffle of feet came toward me. "Dear me, you've spilled your water. Well, no harm done, the glass didn't break."

The overhead light blinded me. I made an effort to focus my gaze on a wavering blob of white uniform with a white cap ludicrously askew on a pompadour of gray hair. How could I have mistaken this fat elderly woman for my husband? "You're my third Special," I deduced in an agony of concentration.

"That's right. You spoke to me when I came, but I guess you don't remember. Mrs. Berry's the name."

"Like in strawberry?"

"Right again."

"Would you turn the light a little out of my eyes?"

"Soon's I get your hypo ready."

Mrs. Berry's hand was large but unsure. "Don't pussy-foot, just wham," I implored her silently.

"There. That should hold you," she said, with a slight wheeze from bending.

"Is it almost morning?"

She peered at her watch. "Far from it. Five minutes lacking two o'clock."

My spirit swooned. "It's a long night. Could you fix my pillows please, they're so uncomfortable."

I felt the enormous cushion of her arm behind my neck as my head snapped forward. "So now, is that better?"

It was worse. Mrs. Berry, whose touch was not a gift to one's body, had created a hollow against the small of my spine, and my limbs fretted to escape the harsh sheet which she had neatened into a trap around me. I sought another way to comfort.

"It's terribly warm in here, I can hardly breathe, it's so warm."

"You try sleeping in a chair and you'll find it plenty

cold," Mrs. Berry remarked. "Besides which, you're running a bit of fever, and that's bound to make you feel hot."

"How much fever?"

Mrs. Berry became every inch the professional. She
straightened her cap and said, "We don't ask questions,
besides which it's not up to me to tell you. Best thing is
to quiet down and let that hypo go to work."

If it only would. Loud and fast, my heart hammered
against my ribs, beating out the minutes for the drug to
take effect. Maybe I hadn't gotten enough of it, maybe
Mrs. Berry had spilled some of it in her ineptness, for the
pain kept tearing into me and through me, and oblivion
eluded me like the teasing arms of a lover. The rhythmic
snoring from across the room started up once more, leaving my mind pinioned to my body, and I wavered crazily
on the borderland of fantasy and reality. There was no
getting away from the sound, it entombed all of me
within the four walls of this hospital room, and fear
caught up with me at last. I was afraid to die, and I was
afraid to live.

I tried to lose the fear in sleep, but memory opened the
floodgates of the past, and suddenly I was no longer myself, I was my mother, and there was a child, hovering
lost and frightened in the shadow of illness, and one child
became all children, and grown men and women became
children in the torment of losing those they loved. "Dear
God, don't let me be a burden. . . ." Prayer was a benefi-
cence. The past receded and the present washed over me
like a tidal wave, bursting the boundaries of thought and
drowning me at last in nothingness.

When I opened my eyes, Miss Sosensky was taking the
patch off the back of my hand. "Good riddance to glucose
and good riddance to hypos," she said. "You're on oral

medication from now on. Here, swallow these couple of capsules and see if they do the job."

I didn't care whether the capsules did their job on the pain, if only they would help to take away the fear that still lay deep and secret within me. "My mother had this operation and never really got over it, she was an invalid for years. . . ." I didn't have the courage to say it. Nobody would tell me the truth anyway. Miss Sosensky wouldn't even tell me what my temperature was, she just squinted at the thermometer and frowned before she took it down. "Oh, by the way," she mentioned, "Mrs. Berry left a message to tell you Hubby telephoned before she went off duty, he wanted to find out what sort of night you had. Say, how long you two been married, anyway?"

"We have grown sons."

"Yeah, they're pretty attentive, too, they keep calling."

The sting of tears burned my eyes. Miss Sosensky noticed. "Look, everybody feels awful after major surgery, stop being sorry for yourself."

She wouldn't have understood if I told her that I wasn't crying out of self-pity, I was crying in pity for the heartache and the worry I was causing.

"Enough weeping in your beer," she went on brusquely. "Let's get busy before the doctor brigade starts." She adjusted the bed so that she could roll the table across it, and then brought me a small basin and my toothbrush, bristles down in a plastic cupful of the crimson mouthwash. "You better enjoy this service while the going's good," she said. "Tomorrow you'll have to walk to the bathroom and do for yourself."

I made a feeble attempt to match the caustic brand of her humor. "My teeth don't really need to be washed, I haven't been using them."

"Very funny. Hurry up, I hear breakfast rattling in the hall."

I shuddered. "I hope not for me."

"Hope again. How do you expect to get your strength back?"

I didn't expect to get my strength back. I hardly ever remembered my mother being up and around. . . .

Miss Sosensky took the tray away. "Okay, baby, don't eat. It's your funeral, not mine."

I closed my eyes against the sharp, sure cut of her tongue. "Hallelujah, those capsules seem to be working," she observed. "I'll run grab myself a cup of coffee."

Quietness came into the room with her absence. The world drifted away.

Half dreaming, I felt my husband's presence. "Are you asleep?" he whispered.

"You can talk out loud," I said, quite jauntily, for the touch of his lips on mine replenished my spirit. "Is Hilda managing all right?"

"Never mind Hilda. Dr. Jones told me you came through the operation beautifully, darling. He even snipped off your appendix, as a sort of bonus for being a good girl."

"What else did he snip off, did he leave me anything?"

"More than enough."

"Enough for what?"

"For all practical purposes. Where's Miss Sosensky?"

"She run grab herself a cup of coffee."

"You are feeling better!"

If only he would go away before the tears started rolling down my cheeks to spoil his happiness. "It's the medicine makes me drowsy, don't mind if I close my eyes a few minutes."

"I don't mind. Go back to sleep, dear." He moved away

from me, and sat in the chair across the room. It was wrong to shut him out, I ought to at least make a pretense of trying to talk to him. I forced my eyes open again, but he was gone. Miss Sosensky was sitting in his place, reading a paperback novel pressed open on the arm of the chair, and knitting an oblong of red wool. I asked her how she managed to be able to do both things at the same time. . . .

"You have to have a little patience," Dr. Smith said. "Give yourself time, you're doing splendidly."

It was upsetting the way nobody kept on being who they were. I rephrased my question to fit the occasion. "How's golf?" I asked him.

"She's still got an anesthesia jag," I heard Miss Sosensky say, only it wasn't Miss Sosensky, it was Miss Kelly.

I was annoyed that she should think I didn't know what I was talking about, and I quickly let her know that I did. "I guess you thought that I said 'golf,'" I said.

15

It was Mary Conlin who finally pulled me out of that hinterland of space where pain, memories and gray-blue capsules compounded a vast unreality. I awoke to a thin, morning sun and recognized her standing at the foot of the bed, staring at me in disbelief. "What's happened, dearie, you were in the pink of health ready to go home when I was here last Wednesday!"

"She was operated Monday," Miss Sosensky answered for me. "Look, if you're going to be around a few minutes, I'll grab a cup of coffee and a doughnut, I didn't have much breakfast."

"I'll make it my business that the patient shouldn't be alone," Mary replied tersely. She waited in grim silence until Miss Sosensky's frugal figure had whisked off behind the screen that partially concealed the open door. "And they call themselves nurses," she said contemptuously. "Hardly a decent one in the lot from the specimens I've run into. Tell me, dearie, how are you feeling?"

"I think I feel better. For the first time." And for the first time, the room was slowly settling into place around me, and I saw people passing in the hall. "Would you close the door, please?"

"Gladly, except it's pretty warm in here, and I remember how you like a room that's nice and fresh."

"I do. I wish I could have a window open."

"And what's to say you can't? I'll lift the one farthest from the bed."

"You won't be able to. It sticks."

"Not if you unloose the little setscrew that holds it. See how easy it goes up?"

"This is wonderful," I said, breathing deep.

"And now we'll have to close the door so's you're not in a draft."

"That's wonderful," I said again.

"It's better a cool room for your flowers as well. My, but they're beautiful!" She thrust an investigating finger into the mossy base of a geometric tower of pink and yellow gladioli. "Dry as a bone, and I wager that goes for the rest of them. Poor things, I'll give them all a bit of a drink while she's gone."

"That's wonderful," I heard myself say for the third time.

"Time was, a nurse took pride in her work, but not any more. Every chance they get they're runnin' out for coffee or a cigarette or sweet talk with the interns. My goodness, I almost put water on this little tree," she broke off, "and if it isn't lemon drops of all things!" She held the small clay pot aloft and peered at it, entranced. "I never saw anything so natural the way the candy's wrapped like little yellow petals, and did you notice the leaves, made of green peppermint!"

"I've been so groggy that I haven't really noticed anything up to now," I confessed. "But I'd love to have you take the tree home with you, Mary, it seems to be about the only thing in the room small enough to carry."

Her face looked as if someone had lit a candle behind her eyes. "Do you mean it? Oh no, I couldn't. It wouldn't be right, depriving you."

"But you'd be doing me a favor, there's so much in here, it's oppressive."

"It's that they're all so grand," she agreed reluctantly. "You can feel more friendly to just a few flowers that are free to stand on their own stems in a vase of honest-to-God water."

"Freesias," I said suddenly. "Do you happen to remember freesias?"

"Freesias? Sure I do. Sort of like little white narcissus, only they smelt sweeter. I haven't seen them around in the longest while."

"Neither have I. I guess they're not stylish any more."

"Ain't it the truth?" She started emptying the basket, and made a face. "Cigarette butts and chewing-gum and wads of tissue with lipstick all over. I only hope Hatchet Face don't smell a rat when she comes back, what with the little tree gone and my watering the flowers and all."

"I don't care if she does," I said recklessly.

Miss Sosensky undoubtedly smelled something when she returned, but it was nothing more than the whiff of fresh air that assaulted her nostrils. She froze briefly on the threshold before she thrust the door against the wall, readjusted the white linen screen, and stalked across the room to bang the window down, knowing exactly where to find the setscrew. "The nerve of these damn cleaning women! Why can't they leave things the way they find them?"

"It wasn't her fault. I asked her to do it."

"Well, thank you so much," Miss Sosensky retorted, "but I don't intend to catch my death of cold sitting in a draft."

I was about to suggest that there wouldn't be a draft with the door closed, but the defiance I had borrowed from Mary's sturdy presence shriveled under the blaze of Miss Sosensky's disapproval. My brain was at last clear of confusion, but an ineffable weariness submerged me. "You're not to go back to sleep," she adjured me sharply, as she opened the closet and dragged the ugly striped bathrobe off its hanger. "You're walking to the bathroom."

I didn't believe at first that she could be in earnest, but to my horror, she really seemed to mean it. "Come on," she said. "Sit up and put your arms through."

I warded her off. "Please, no, I can't, I don't feel able to."

"Too bad about you, other surgical cases manage to feel able to. Hurry up before your breakfast comes." Her bony arm hoisted me free of the pillows, and swung my legs over the side of the bed. The familiar position wakened echoes of my confinements, when I was allowed to "dangle" in preparation for the truly big event of sitting in a chair drawn close and blanket-draped to receive me. There was no "dangling" in this procedure. Before I knew what was happening, my feet landed on the floor with my knees buckling beneath me. Miss Sosensky stood behind me. "Just keep going, you won't bust your stitches, if that's what you're afraid of."

Drenched with sweat, I reached the basin, and lifted the toothbrush to my lips. "Now let me get back to bed," I implored.

"Not so fast," she said. "You sit over there in the armchair while I change your sheets."

"I couldn't!"

She was adamant. "Listen. You got away with murder yesterday because you were running a little fever, but your temperature's down to normal, so don't expect me to break my back again making up the bed with you in it."

Desperately I clung to the headboard and to one last

hope. "Wouldn't it be better to have my sponge bath before you put on clean linen?"

"You let me worry about your sponge bath. Patients who try to run the show give me a pain in the you-know-where."

I tried to keep my voice from quavering. "If I have to do it, couldn't you move the chair a little closer?"

"Oh, stop making such a fuss over a few little steps."

"But I don't think I can manage it."

"Okay, so I'll catch you if you faint."

I had never fainted in my life, and some remaining vestige of pride kept me upright in the crumbling jigsaw of walls and floor and ceiling. My teeth chattered as I sank into the chair. "Could I have a blanket? I'm cold."

"For the love of Pete, a few minutes ago you were complaining you were so hot." She yanked one of the brown covers from the bed, and tossed it over to me. "Honestly, if you're not the limit."

Maybe I really was the limit, I thought abjectly. I hadn't meant to be unreasonable, and I felt sickened by Miss Sosensky's loud silence of hostility as I watched her strip off the used sheets and fling them into a corner.

The orderly brought the breakfast tray. "You might as well eat in the chair as long as you're up," Miss Sosensky said. "Cream of wheat. Good and nourishing."

I lifted a spoonful of the congealed white cereal to my lips. My stomach revolted. I felt exposed, almost degraded in my weakness. From where I sat, I could see an occasional early-morning visitor unable to resist a furtive glance into the room. If only Miss Sosensky would close the door. I was afraid to ask her. I despised myself for being afraid.

I hid my misery and my shame in trying to gulp down a little of the tepid coffee. And then Dr. Jones walked in, and I could have burst into tears of relief and joy, but kind and reassuring as I remembered him to have been the evening before the operation, he did not deliver me from Miss Sosensky's dominion.

"Well, well, this is more like it," he said, not at all appalled at finding me out of bed. "Quite an improvement over yesterday, isn't it, nurse?"

"You wouldn't think so if you saw what a job it was to get her to the bathroom and over to the chair," Miss Sosensky replied.

"That's to be expected." He smiled and patted my shoulder. "On the whole, I'm very pleased with you. Keep up the good work, and I'll stop by again on my evening rounds."

I wanted to hold on to his hand and talk to him for a few minutes alone, but Miss Sosensky seized the initiative. "I'd like to have a word with you in the hall, Doctor."

He said, "Certainly." She followed him from the room and when she returned she looked satisfied with whatever it was she had accomplished in her private report. "You can get back to bed now," she announced.

She made no move to lift the blanket from my knees or to roll the table out of my way. "I'll need some help," I said.

"You're the sort of patient who could keep two nurses busy all day long, aren't you?"

I bit my lips.

"I took care of another lulu of a dame a couple of weeks ago, right in this hospital. She could have stood under the shower as easy as not, but would she? Oh no, she had to get her money's worth, and have bed baths. I told her to ask the registry to send somebody else in my place, I wasn't going to be taken advantage of. Not much I wasn't."

Miss Sosensky finished off with a toss of her head, and I got the message clearly: one more preposterous request, and she would walk off the case. It was intolerable to put up with such insolence, and it took all my control not to dismiss her then and there. But how could I be so sure that I hadn't been overly fractious and demanding? I could feel the poison of self-doubt slowly destroying my confidence, and I kept silent. I wanted only to reach the haven of bed, quickly and inconspicuously, without giving her any further cause for complaint.

I lay shivering with weakness after she had whipped off the striped bathrobe and carried it back to the closet. Then she stood looking down at me inimically. "Now what?"

"Nothing."

My throat felt parched, but with effort I was able to lift the glass of water on the thermos tray. Although it had bubbles of staleness in it, I didn't dare ask her to replenish it, nor did I dare ask for a fresh gown, much less a sponge bath. It was almost a relief when she turned away from me and settled herself in the armchair with her book and her knitting. Her needles began flashing in and out of the red wool, and I was glad I wasn't the red wool.

16

The minutes dragged by. My small traveling clock had been moved to the desk, and I couldn't see what time it was, but according to breakfast it must be well after ten. I couldn't understand why my husband hadn't come yet —he always stopped in early on his way to the office. Visions of an accident or a sudden heart attack haunted my imagination, and when finally I heard the clatter of lunch dishes in the hall, I was frantic with worry.

"Chicken breast, baked potato and jello," Miss Sosensky recited in an elaborate monotone, plumping the tray in front of me. "You'll only pick at it anyway, so I might as well go for my own lunch."

I hid my panic until she had whisked out of the room. There was only one thing to do. I would manage to get to the telephone booth next to the elevator and call my husband's office, and if he wasn't there, I'd call Hilda. . . . And then I heard his step, and saw him standing in the doorway, and like a fool I burst into tears. "You didn't come this morning, I was so worried, I thought something dreadful had happened to you. . . ."

"Now wait a minute, wait a minute," he tried to calm me, "you knew I wasn't going to be here until noon."

I wiped my eyes on his handkerchief. "I did? Then I must be losing my memory, and that's something to really cry about. When did you tell me?"

"I didn't. I told Miss Sosensky to tell you when I spoke to her over the phone around eight thirty this morning."

"She forgot," I said bloodlessly.

"She forgot? Well, dammit, she had no right to forget!"

"It wouldn't have happened if I had the telephone back in the room. And it's a nuisance for the nurses, too, to have to keep running to the desk for messages."

"That's too bad," he said dryly. "I'm afraid they'll have to put up with it."

"But why can't the phone be reconnected?"

"Because too many people call, and Dr. Jones believes in complete quiet for the first few days."

I began to laugh hysterically. "Complete quiet, and he lets me get up and walk around!"

"I don't believe it," my husband said flatly.

"Neither did I, until I found myself doing it. It seems to be something new after operations."

"I bet it hurt."

"I wasn't exactly stoical about it," I admitted obliquely.

His loyalty was beautiful. "I wouldn't have been either," he said. He seemed to feel that the occasion deserved a little privacy, and moved to the door to close it.

"Don't," I stopped him importunately. "It'll make the room too hot—"

"It's stifling in here anyway. Is there any reason you can't have a window open?"

"Yes. She'd be furious."

"Who'd be furious?"

"Miss Sosensky," I said tremulously, and then the whole wretched story poured out of me. "I didn't mean to complain or worry you about it," I ended up, with a hiccough of pure misery, "but I just don't feel strong enough to stand up to her. I'm even afraid to ask for anything, or she'd think I was too demanding, and walk off the case."

On the rarest occasions have I seen my husband's eyes turn into cold slate, and his jaw set in the granite of controlled fury. "Where are you going?" I called after him apprehensively.

"To get a few things straightened out."

I wished I could have stopped him, I didn't want him to start a fuss, it would only make matters worse. Nervously, I pulled at the cellulose band around my wrist; it would be a kind of catharsis if I finally succeeded in ridding myself of it. No chance.

He came back. He said grimly, "I found out from the floor supervisor that this isn't Miss Sosensky's first offense in intimidating a patient, but nothing was done about it because in this cockeyed world it seems that patients are more expendable than nurses."

"But patients can be unreasonable too," I said, in a valiant effort to be fair to her. "Why not just forget the whole thing?"

"No," he said firmly. "This time she's gone too far. She's through."

"You mean she's quit?"

"She's fired."

"You're just saying that to spare my feelings. She really did walk off the case, didn't she?"

"Of course not, she was bluffing."

"Then what did happen outside?"

"If you'll shut up long enough, I'll tell you."

"I'll shut up," I said meekly. "Go on."

"The supervisor advised me to call Dr. Jones, and luckily I reached him at his office. He said he'd never worked with Miss Sosensky before, but he hadn't liked her attitude when she cornered him in the hall this morning."

"He didn't? Oh, that's such a relief, I was so afraid he'd believe everything she told him."

"He has no illusions about nurses."

"And they used to be so wonderful," I brooded.

"According to Dr. Jones, there are a few who still are. Luckily, he happens to be able to get hold of a very good one who just came off of one of his cases. She'll be here in the morning."

I groped again for his handkerchief. "You'll never know how degraded I felt for being so craven."

"Sick people aren't craven," he said. "They're helpless."

Miss Sosensky marched in at that moment. The air sizzled around her. She snatched up her knitting and her book and thrust them into her voluminous bag, and without a look or word to either of us she marched out again.

I couldn't help feeling sorry, and I was glad that my husband felt no triumph in her departure either. "It's an ugly thing to have happened," he said soberly. "Try to put it out of your mind."

I tried, but it wasn't easy. Miss Kelly came on duty at four, bustling in with her usual chirpy greeting. I concluded that she hadn't heard about my run-in with Miss Sosensky until she glanced up from her crossword puzzle a little later, and mentioned that she wouldn't be seeing me after tomorrow. Then I was certain that I had become a pariah among patients. I tried to hide my agitation, but my voice came out in a small croak. "Is it because I'm difficult that you're leaving?"

"Good grief, no," she said, "you're not much trouble."

Her words were like a welcome balm on a raw wound, but when she went on to say that she never worked on weekends, my heart sank anew. While I remained in the hospital, I could, if necessary, rely on floor care, but what was going to happen when I was eventually permitted to leave? I had already gathered that the majority of nurses shunned the headache of accepting cases at home, and I had discomfiting visions of my daughters-in-law dutifully taking turns to sit with me during my long convalescence.

I slept fitfully that night, careful, however, that Mrs. Berry should enjoy her uninterrupted rest. Anyway, there was nothing she could do to alleviate either the nag of physical discomfort or the mental trepidation that I might not be able to please my new eight-to-four Special.

17

At first I thought she was one of the aides—an unusually ingratiating aide—with a velvety voice and a dark brown velvety skin. "I'm Mrs. Packleford, Georgina Packleford, but my patients call me Packy," she introduced herself in a flowing cadence that could only have originated in Virginia.

"I'm so glad you were free to come," I said, hoping my surprise didn't show.

She had a smile full of good, white teeth. "Dr. Jones sure was right quick getting me before I went on another case," she said.

"And I'm sure grateful to him," I smiled back at her.

She straightened the covers, and took my temperature, not making any mystery about it. "Any more normal and you'd be sick," she said.

My heart lifted. "I'm just loafing."

"You sure are, it's shameful to waste this expensive pill on you." She poured some fresh water from the thermos. "You swallow good," she complimented me. "Some patients make a big production getting a little capsule down their throat. Would you like for me to help you walk to the bathroom now, or rest a little longer? No hurry, breakfast won't be coming for nearly an hour yet."

"I think I'd like to wait a little, I foolishly didn't sleep well," I admitted. "That is, if it doesn't set you back," I remembered my manners.

"What kind of talk is that? I'm here for you to suit yourself, hon, not me."

I liked the way the "hon" slipped in, unobtrusive and friendly, without a trace of condescension. "Anyway, I got plenty to do, till you're ready," she said. "How about a window open a little, it's like a spring day out."

"I'd love it. Mrs. Berry—that's my night nurse—has sinus and can't stand fresh air."

"Mighty peculiar she can stand to have these radiators hissing away. I'm turning them off, all this heat's bound to wither your flowers. My, but they're pretty, and so many of them."

"Many too many. I asked Miss Kelly if we could send them to the children's ward, but she said the orderlies were busy and couldn't bother moving them."

"Well, that ain't necessarily so. Leastways not when you got connections," Packy added with a wink. "I'll tend to it soon's I get you comfortable."

"Would you see first if all the cards have been taken off? There should be a pile of them in the top desk drawer."

She made a quick survey, and opened the drawer to add a small envelope that had escaped notice. "Looks like you got your work cut out for you, with this big bunch you got to thank for."

"My husband's going to have the letters typed at his office," I confessed ignobly. "I'll just sign them. I don't feel up to writing."

"Not yet, maybe, but you will after you get home."

"Whenever that will be."

"Sooner than you think. My daughter only stayed in

the hospital three days after her baby—and a plenty big baby, too, nine pounds eleven ounces."

"My daughter-in-law stayed five days and I thought that was unheard of," I compared notes eagerly, omitting to say that my grandchild weighed in at a mere six pounds nine ounces. "But of course," I qualified, "having babies isn't the same as having everything you ever had them with taken out in one fell swoop."

"I grant you that, hon. I'm plain lucky, I still got what the good Lord started me off with. Except for one breast that had to come off with cancer.

"Oh. I'm sorry," I said, and added with difficulty, "Then maybe I'm lucky, too."

"Everybody is lucky even when they ain't," Packy asserted sagely. "I learned that when I started nursing. Listen, you reckon I can leave you a few minutes while I round up a certain young feller to tote these flowers down to the ward?"

"For goodness' sake, yes."

My husband came and found me alone. His face fell. "She didn't show up."

"She sure did, hon!"

"Another coffee grabber," he deduced sourly.

"Guess again," I said.

When Packy came back from her errand, he saw for himself that I wasn't trying to make the best of a bad bargain. "That orderly promise me he come soon as he can," she said. "But I got to tell you this room is going to look mighty bare unless folks happen to send more flowers pretty quick."

"If folks don't," my husband told her, "you let me know when I telephone later, and I'll bring some this evening."

He didn't have to. According to Packy, the good Lord saw fit to immediately fill the vacant expanse of the bureau with a metal container fitted into a raffia canoe that was stuffed to the gills with a passionate combination of blue heather, birds of paradise, and some truly lovely but ill-advised water lilies that were already beginning to droop on their firmly corseted stems. "They not goin' to live long," Packy lamented. "Water lilies naturally meant to lay down, not stand up."

"It's a sin, wiring them to death like that," I agreed, and urged her to take them home and try to revive them. She consented readily, but when a huge basket of fruit followed on the heels of the canoe, she refused to rape its magnificence by so much as a single orange. "But I won't eat any of it, and it'll only smell up the room," I told her.

"Fruit do smell, sure enough, when there's a lot of it," she conceded. "How about if I carry it out to the desk like it is, and the nurses and interns can all help theirselves, and me too, if I want."

"Would they like it?" I asked doubtfully.

"Like it? There's goin' to be a regular free-for-all scramble the minute they set eyes on it."

"Untie the card and take it out now—wait a second, is that a bunch of hothouse grapes?"

Packy appraised the luscious purple globules draped gracefully across the top of the basket. "I can't rightly say about the hothouse part," she debated, "on account of I bought a bunch for my daughter, pretty near as nice, from the vegetable stand on my corner."

Times had certainly changed, I pondered, not for the first time in the past several months. It was nothing unusual these days for children to shoot up to six feet tall before they reached their middle teens, and ordinary grapes to grow as large as small purple plums, and people to get out of bed before they were hardly off the operating table.

And that was only the half of it. Dr. Smith came in to see me late Sunday evening, and told me that I would be going home the following Tuesday.

I thought he must have lost his senses, to say nothing of my having lost my tongue. "Look here," he finally demanded, "aren't you delighted at the prospect of leaving?"

"I don't think I feel up to it," I stammered. "I mean I didn't expect it to be this soon, I was only operated last Monday!"

"And eight days," he said, "falls within the usual range of hospitalization following the majority of surgical cases. Barring complications, of course."

"But I know someone who had ordinary shingles, and she was flat on her back at the Park Hill for two full weeks!"

"True. On the theory that it sometimes takes longer to cure a head cold than a lobar pneumonia."

I stared at him helplessly, while he leaned forward to peer at me in mock amazement. "Do my eyes deceive me, or are you the same unruly patient who's been raising the roof to get out of here?"

"Yes, but that was before I realized I was really ill and needed an operation."

"You were ill before you were operated on," he corrected me, "but all you need now is a sufficient period of recuperation, and an intelligent approach toward resuming your normal activities. Surgery of this nature frequently takes an emotional as well as a physical toll of one's reserves."

I was uncomfortably aware that he was giving me more than my allotted share of his time, but he had also given me the opening that I needed. "Dr. Smith, that's what's been preying on my mind," I came out with it. "Exactly how much of a toll?"

"The tumor was not malignant," he said firmly.

"I know. I don't mean that."

"Then what else is bothering you?"

"You took my history the first day I came to your office—"

He nodded. "That's routine procedure."

"Well, if you remember, my mother had to have the same operation I had, and she never got over it, she was an invalid until her death."

"Quite possible. After effects of one kind or another were not infrequent following complete hysterectomies."

"I know. And what I'm asking is whether I'm going to have any after effects. Please be frank with me, Dr. Smith."

"I'll be frank with you. The after effects in your case will be largely of your own choosing."

"You mean I can be as sick as I want for as long as I want."

His smile was, I noticed suddenly, not entirely devoid of charm. "Very aptly put," he said. "And if I may be blunt as well as frank—"

"Go ahead."

"Dr. Jones and I both feel that you are not only ready to go home, but we need your bed for patients who need it more than you. However, you mustn't feel that we're in any way minimizing the seriousness of what you've been through," he hastened to assure me, "nor do I pretend to ignore the fact that you're facing a difficult crisis in a woman's life. Men approximate similar readjustments, although not in the same terms or to the same degree. Also, the psychological impact is not apt to be as obvious; a man frequently compensates in the hobbies he develops."

"I see," I said.

He rose and held out his hand. "I'll stop by again before you leave."

"Dr. Smith, one more thing before you go—what about nurses when I get home?"

"Until you regain your strength, I should say it might be advisable but not essential, especially since I noticed on your chart that you've been doing very nicely without Specials."

"It wasn't choice," I confessed. "Miss Kelly and Mrs. Berry don't work on weekends, and the registry had no one else to send."

"That's par for the course."

"I still have my eight-to-four nurse, though."

"Splendid. By all means keep her on, provided she's willing to work outside the hospital.—May I?" He paused to pinch off a white carnation, and stuck it in his buttonhole. It went nicely with his sunburn.

Remind me to remind myself, I said to myself, not to get mad at doctors who play golf.

18

I asked Packy as soon as she came on duty the next morning whether she would go home with me. I had a little palpitation while I waited for her answer, because I could see she wasn't crazy about the idea. "Sure, hon, I'll take you home. And I reckon if you need me to," she agreed without enthusiasm, "I'll stay on the same as here."

"You couldn't stay all day?"

"Then who'd baby-sit with little Georgie? You recollect I told you my daughter leaves for her waitress job soon's I get back from work."

"Oh, yes. That's right."

"But you got a cook or somebody to look after you and answer the telephone when I quit at four, don't you?"

Hilda was no cordon bleu or Florence Nightingale, but she was certainly Johnny-on-the-spot with a telephone. "I guess it's just that I'm going to miss ringing for the floor nurse—even if she doesn't come."

Packy rolled her eyes. "Ain't it the truth," she said.

"Oh, dear."

"What's wrong?"

"I just happened to think I won't be here when Mary Conlin comes on Wednesday."

"Who's Mary Conlin?"

"She's the substitute for the scrap baskets."

"You tickle me," Packy said. "Look, I got a good idea.

Let's put on that slinky blue kimono in the closet—which I ain't seen you in yet—and surprise your husband when he gets here and take a little walk up and down the hall with him."

I did not think that my husband would particularly enjoy the "surprise" of piloting a slinky blue kimono up and down the hall. "Let's not," I said.

A hospital gown had its points. It was easy to get in and out of, and didn't have to be lived up to with powder and lipstick.

Tuesday came too soon. Packy shook the thermometer down and looked gratified.

"No temperature," I surmised ruefully.

"You want some?"

"A little. Just enough to keep me here."

Packy gave her throaty laugh. "You sure are a cutup."

I wasn't a cutup. I was in deadly earnest.

Another of the many hospital regulations specified that rooms had to be vacated before noon, but as the next occupant of seventeen twenty-one was not scheduled to arrive until late in the day, Dr. Smith had arranged for me to remain on until after lunch.

"That suits me just dandy," Packy rejoiced. "It gives you time to eat—if how you pick at your tray can rightly be called eating—and it gives me time to get you home and into bed before I go off duty."

It also gave my husband time to go to his office in the morning before attending to the necessary business of checking me out—a procedure that proved to be almost as tedious as the checking in.

Packy helped me to get dressed while he went down to the cashier's office to pay the final bill. It was a formidable accounting that ran over onto two long pages, and added up to a total that looked like a telephone number. Aunt Aggie was right, you really did have to be a millionaire to be sick these days.

I felt strange in street clothes, and Packy, in street clothes, seemed strange to me, too. I remembered how Miss Sisson used to lose her aura of sanctity when she traded her winged cap and crisp white uniform for a brown coat embellished by a skinny mink scarf.

"What's the matter, hon?"

"Nothing. Why?"

"You look a million miles away someplace. You should be thinking about how nice it is you're going home."

"My thoughts keep jumping around. I guess I'm a little scared."

"Lots of patients feel scared this quick after a big operation."

"One good thing"—I masked my fear by voicing it—"I won't have to worry about dieting."

Packy's diplomacy was commendable. "On account of I didn't see you before, I can't tell one speck of difference."

She didn't have to have seen me "before." My tweed suit hung on me and a dismayed glance in the mirror told me that my face was all cheekbones. I hoped that my husband wouldn't be shocked at the sight of me, up and dressed. Lying against pillows in a fluffy bed-jacket blanketed the hollows and the gauntness.

Although he couldn't help but notice the scarecrow in a wheel chair waiting to be transported into a taxi, he pretended not to notice. Hilda, however, was not schooled in hiding her middle-European emotions. We could hear her rushing to the door at the first sound of the key in the latch, and when she saw me standing with

Packy's arm around me, her eyes brimmed. "Ach," she said brokenly, "is good you are home again."

"Thank you, Hilda. This is Mrs. Packleford."

It was an awkward moment, for "Mrs. Packleford" was far from Hilda's idea of a registered trained nurse. Some sort of Teutonic revolution was bound to arise during Packy's eight-hour span of authority, but I was in no state to think about it. The universe shredded around me as I battled anew the disoriented sensations that had assailed me driving away from the hospital. Confusion lurked in the hurrying crowds, the traffic tangles, the belching of black smoke from the high buildings. Nothing and no one had changed except me. I had lost step with reality, I was an outsider emerging from a world apart. My own home had lost its familiarity; it was as if I were a stranger, entering it for the first time.

"Careful," my husband warned. "Hilda was polishing the floors like a whirlwind when I left this morning. They're slippery, hold on to me."

I held on to him, thankful for his solidness and his strength. Packy walked ahead of us to steal a peep into the dining room. "Lordy, Lordy," she reverted to idiom, "this is a sure beautiful place."

When she reached the bedroom she became ecstatic. "It's just like a picture out of a book with a real live fire in the fireplace. And will you look at that bunch of yellow roses! If you ask me, they's prettier than all the flowers you got in the hospital all put together."

"Yes," I said. My knees were rubber, and I was shivering. Never mind the roses, I wanted only to reach the warmth of the flaming logs without shaking to pieces. My husband drew an ottoman close to the comfortable wing chair. "I'm fine," I told him unsteadily.

"I know you are, but put your feet up anyway."

"That's a good idea, you rest awhile 'til I unpack," Packy chimed in. "You got to remember it's going to take a little time to get to feeling like yourself again."

"If I ever get to feeling like myself again," I thought unhappily.

Efficiently, Packy emptied the suitcase, and with a sixth sense found the right place for everything, while Hilda stood watching like an angry fifth wheel. "Now I better start getting you into bed." Packy closed the closet door and glanced anxiously at her watch. Hilda jumped to the kill. "Yah, is almost four o'clock. You shouldn't be late."

With effort, I rallied to Packy's defense. "Mrs. Packleford has to get home to look after her grandchild."

"Otherwise, I'd be glad to stay, it's just that I can't," she explained.

Hilda had the grace to soften. "Then better you go," she said, "I can do what is to do." She folded the spread, turned down the covers, and thriftily unearthed one of my old nightgowns, arranging it punctiliously across the foot of the bed.

"Much obliged," Packy thanked her. "You sure you're all right, hon?"

She lingered, uneasy about leaving. "Now you got my number, just in case you want to call me for anything?"

"I have it," my husband answered, "but we won't need it."

"Of course not, I'm fine." I tried to smile, but my lips were dry with apprehension. With Packy no longer at my side, how could I conceal this nakedness of fear? A memory, nebulous and tormenting, drowned me in dark turmoil. What elusive association caused the palms of my hands to grow wet, and my heart to hammer up into my throat? And then suddenly it came to me—I had felt like that about Miss Sisson, and Packy was the nearest to Miss Sisson that I could ever hope to find in a world where the Miss Sosenskys had taken over. "I'm ashamed of being craven," I had told my husband, and he had comforted me by saying, "Sick people aren't craven, they're helpless."

Perhaps, I thought, sick people also become children, seeking refuge from the obligation of maturity.

"Now mind you don't sit up too long. Get right into bed, and a cup of hot tea wouldn't do you any hurt."

Slowly, I returned from that vast hinterland of space, finding my way through cobwebs of confusion. "And it wouldn't do you any hurt to stop being such an old fuss-box," I retorted with bravado. "If you're going, go."

"Okay, but don't forget your pill at half past four."

"I'll see that she takes it," my husband promised.

"Well . . ."—Packy buttoned her coat—"I'll be here in the morning, eight o'clock sharp, maybe earlier if anyone's up to let me in."

"I am always in the kitchen at quarter to seven," Hilda said stiffly.

"We have an early breakfast," I injected, like an automatic buffer, and I suddenly thought how nice it was going to be not to have to wait until nine o'clock for a cup of coffee.

On the way to bed, I paused for a moment beside the crystal vase of yellow roses, and bent to inhale the delicate richness of their fragrance. "Strong, lovely long stems in lovely, clear water," I murmured.

"Then you do like them," my husband said.

I looked at him in surprise. "I love them! How could you think I wouldn't?"

"You didn't seem to pay any attention to them."

"I must have been too busy paying attention to myself," I said.

19

It could have been any number of things that gradually gave me the feeling of being home, where I belonged. It could have been the telescoping of a whole lifetime in those moments of agony in the easy chair by the fire; it could have been the yellow roses; it could even have been the welcoming embrace of a soft mattress and downy pillows. "Paradise couldn't be more heavenly," I sighed. "No tea, Hilda, please."

"Maybe it is better that you do not spoil your appetite," she said. "I am bringing your tray at half past five, like in the hospital."

"You are bringing my tray nothing of the kind at half past five. We'll have dinner at the same time we always do."

"Not on your first night," my husband objected.

"Then we'll compromise, this once. Six thirty, Hilda."

She nodded sagely. "That is good. I do not like to rush with my cooking or keep it too long hot in the oven, it dries up."

Surely my ears had deceived me. Could Hilda have actually learned, in my absence, to adopt this basic rule of food preparation? In spite of my patient tutelage, she had persistently scaled her culinary endeavors to her own ingenious system of short cuts, so surely this was another instance of the broom sweeping clean, and she would shortly revert to her slapdash methods. I wondered, weary at the very thought of it, how long it would be before I had the will, or the strength, to supervise again the running of my household.

"Pill." My husband was standing at my side with a glass of water and a capsule.

"You know something? I don't think I need it," I discovered.

"Packy said to."

"Never mind what Packy said. I'll take the telephone instead."

"No telephoning until tomorrow."

"But I don't want to wait until tomorrow to call San Francisco."

"That's all, though." He placed the instrument within my reach, and I lifted the receiver only to put it down again.

"What's the matter?"

"Hilda's telling all her friends and relatives I'm back from the hospital."

"I'll go ask her to hang up."

"Oh, let her talk, I can wait. I keep forgetting there's three hours' difference in time." I indulged in a long, luxurious stretching of my bones. "I can't get over how wonderful it is all of a sudden to be home."

"You dreaded it, didn't you?"

"And I tried so hard to hide it," I admitted.

"You needn't have. You shouldn't have," he said.

"But it seemed so unnatural to feel that way."

"It would have been more unnatural not to feel that way. An operation like that is a big shock to your system. To my system too," he added with a wry smile.

"I'm sorry," I said contritely. "I only hope I'm not going

to put you through any more worry. I mean I hope I'm not going to have to be waited on, or bedridden, or anything," I confessed to the fear that was still haunting me.

"I wouldn't count on it," he said cheerfully. "A week ago yesterday you were babbling your way out of the anesthetic, and in another week you'll be going to Dr. Jones's office to have the clamps removed, and after that you can take a real bath in the bathtub and you'll be as good as new."

He was making it all sound entirely too unimportant. "And just where did you get all this interesting information?" I inquired off the top of my voice.

He ran his reply into a single word. "Dr. Jones Dr. Smith and Dr. Harris."

"Dr. Harris. That pompous little pip-squeak."

"Now you're beginning to sound like your old self."

I smoldered in retrospect as I enumerated the various indignities to which I'd been needlessly subjected. "What was the point of having to have all those tests and X rays all over again when I'd just had them, that's what really burnt me up."

"Whether it was or wasn't necessary," he said soberly, "don't underestimate the functioning of a hospital. It's a good place to land in when you need it."

"If you survive," I amended tartly.

"People do," he said. "You have, for one. Be grateful."

It took a long moment for the answer to come. "I'm grateful," I acknowledged humbly.

"That makes two of us," he said.

Hilda, emanating the satisfied aura of telephonic saturation, appeared at the door. "Is very nice maybe, if I fix two trays so you can eat together."

"Is even nicer maybe if you fix no trays, and we eat together in the dining room," I all at once decided.

Hilda turned to my husband. "That is all right, you think so?"

He didn't think so. "Wait until tomorrow before you try sitting up at the table," he said. "Don't overdo your first night home."

"Overdo?" I scoffed. "What's overdoing, to eat like a human being? Hilda, bring me that slinky blue kimono from the closet."

"Yah, with all the little pleats. . . ." She gave the impression of skating across the room and skating back again. "Something else?"

"Mirror, lipstick and rouge. And you," I told my husband, "can be one up on a cocktail while I'm getting ready."

"Sit by the fire until I come back for you."

"I don't have to sit by the fire, stop treating me like an invalid."

I was only a little shaky as I walked the length of the hall and joined him in the living room. We sat quietly enjoying the blessedness of reunion until Hilda announced that supper was on the table getting cold.

She had changed from her usual cotton uniform into black rayon, organdy apron and frilly cap, and looked every inch her salary. She served the first course on our best Royal Doulton, and passed the crackers on a silver plate, and the iced celery on a Waterford dish. Responsibility became her vastly.

"Hilda, this is marvelous soup," I exclaimed with the first taste. "I didn't know you had it in you!"

"I did not make the soup," she reluctantly admitted. "Your Aunt Aggie sent it over this morning, she said I must give it to you tonight."

My husband lifted a spoonful of the golden liquid to

his lips. "And you threw a whole jarful of it down the toilet!" he accused me wrathfully.

"It's convenient for you to forget that you were too high and mighty to carry it home!"

It was very much like old times, except that Hilda distinguished herself beyond all expectations. The lamb chops were crisp and brown, neither overdone nor underdone, and the mashed potatoes fluffy and nutmeg-seasoned, as I had taught her repeatedly, and as she had as repeatedly forgotten.

"I'm starved," I said. "Hilda, everything is delicious. Perfect."

"I am glad," Hilda acknowledged simply. "I tried."

"Do you think"—an inspiration came to me—"that you could possibly manage if I telephoned Mrs. Packleford not to come back in the morning? I happen to know Dr. Jones wants her for a case that needs her more than I do."

Hilda stopped short on her way to the kitchen. The expression on her face was eloquent. She said, emphatically, "It will be easier for me without a nurse to get in my way."

"Don't push yourself," my husband warned me.

"I won't."

He leaned across the table to put his hand on mine. "And don't put on an act for me."

"I'm not."

"Then tell me the truth. How do you really feel?"

"Fine," I almost said. It was the answer always quick on my lips, glib and thoughtless, because I had never before been conscious of health, or ill health. Now I sought for a more considered response to the troubled query in his eyes.

"Remember. I want the truth."

I gave him the truth. "I feel well," I said.

Ha